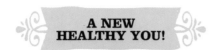

A NEW
HEALTHY YOU!

Sugar
Free

iglaabooks

Published in 2017
by Igloo Books Ltd
Cottage Farm
Sywell
NN6 0BJ
www.igloobooks.com

Cover images: (bl) Westend61 / © Getty images
Additional cover and interior imagery: © iStock / Getty images

HUN001 1017
2 4 6 8 10 9 7 5 3 1
ISBN 978-1-78810-615-3

Cover designed by Nicholas Gage
Edited by Jasmin Peppiatt

Printed and manufactured in China

Contents

Introduction

Introduction 6

Why cut out sugar? 8

Types of sugar 10

How much is enough? 12

Going sugar-free 14

Reading food labels.....................18

What not to eat 20

Low-sugar stars........................... 22

Fruit: friend or foe 24

Eating out.................................. 26

Being active, staying safe................. 28

Keeping motivated 32

Recipes

Breakfasts and brunches.................. 34

Lunches and light bites 48

Main meals.................................. 70

Desserts 88

Treats 104

Meal plans and diary

Meal plan and diary 112

Keep it off 126

Introduction

You've probably heard a lot about sugar in the news recently. Obesity is on the rise, along with diabetes and heart disease. Many of these problems are being blamed on eating too much sugar. You may think that you keep your sugar intake under control, but many of us do not realise just how much sugar is hidden in the food we eat.

A growing problem

For thousands of years, people ate very little sugar. Honey was used sparingly as a sweetener. However, in the last couple of centuries, as refined sugar has become cheaper and more readily available, our sugar intake has massively increased. Now, many people with busy lives rely on processed food for convenience and many of these foods are loaded with hidden sugar.

What to do?

If you go online, you will find a lot of conflicting advice. It can be hard to make sense of all the different opinions out there. The one thing that most experts agree on is that too much sugar is bad for you. Cutting down on the amount of sugar you eat is certainly not going to hurt you and it could help you improve your overall health.

Many people are choosing to take the plunge and cut sugar from their diet. Some try to eliminate sugar completely; many cut refined sugar from their diets; and others do their best to get their intake within recommended guidelines. Most people who cut down on sugar say that they feel better and look great as a result. Why not try it for yourself?

Why cut out sugar?

There are a wide variety of reasons for cutting sugar from your diet: to improve your overall health, to lose weight or even to reduce the risk of serious illnesses. Most of us eat more sugar than we should, but not everyone realises the consequences this has on our bodies.

Many foods that contain added sugar have a lot of calories with few other nutrients. Eating too much of these foods can make you overweight, which can lead to a whole host of health problems. One study found that a person's risk of dying from heart disease increased along with the percentage of sugar in their diet – no matter how young or active they were.

Diabetes is the other big risk associated with eating too much sugar. Our bodies produce insulin to help break down sugar. A person with diabetes cannot produce enough insulin to cope with the sugar they eat. Left untreated, diabetes can cause complications such as stroke, nerve damage, blindness and kidney disease.

Take care of your teeth

Sugary foods and drinks are a major cause of tooth decay. Your mouth is naturally full of bacteria and when you 'feed' the bacteria with sugary foods and drinks, they break down the sugars and produce acid. This acid can decay the surface of your teeth, causing cavities. Brushing regularly will help prevent this, but it is also important to limit your sugar intake.

DO WE NEED SUGAR?

Calories are a measure of the energy a food contains. Sugar provides energy that we need, but it is only one source of energy. We should aim to get most of our calories from other foods, such as lean proteins, starchy foods, fruits and vegetables.

Types of sugar

When you think of sugar, you probably think of white granulated sugar, but sugar actually comes in many different forms. Some types are found naturally in foods, while others are added during cooking or processing.

Most of the sugar that we add to our food is sucrose, which comes from either sugar cane or sugar beets. The juice is extracted from the plants and impurities are removed. Then the juice is crystallised into what we call 'refined sugar'. Whether it comes from sugar cane or sugar beets, the end product is identical. Demerara sugar and brown sugar are made using the same process. They are slightly less refined but still full of empty calories.

Not created equally

The glycaemic index (GI) measures by how much, gram for gram, a substance raises your blood glucose level compared to glucose. Foods with a high glycaemic index, such as sucrose, are broken down quickly and release glucose rapidly into the bloodstream, giving you a 'sugar rush' that quickly fades. Foods with a low glycaemic index release glucose slowly, giving you energy over a much longer period of time.

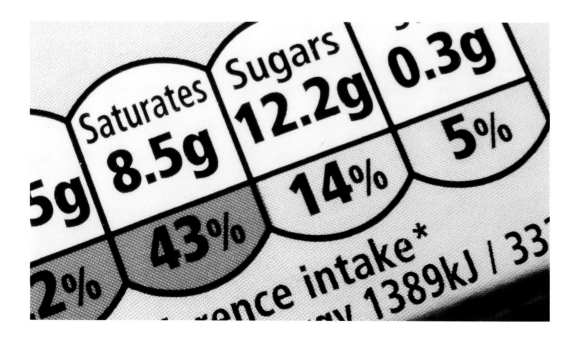

Natural sugars

Fruit contains a type of sugar called fructose. Fructose occurs naturally in the fruit and is not added. Fructose has a lower glycaemic index than sucrose, so it is safer for diabetics, but everyone should still limit the amount of fructose they eat.

SUGAR SUBSTITUTES

Scientists have developed a range of substances with the sweetness of sugar but fewer calories. If you love the taste of sweet things, these artificial sweeteners can deliver the taste of sugar with virtually no calories. They do not harm your teeth and diabetics can eat them more safely than sugar. However, they are best eaten in moderation. Stevia, a sugar substitute from the stevia plant, is a natural product with many of the same benefits. Agave nectar, brown rice syrup and maple syrup are all examples of sugar substitutes that release energy more slowly than sugar.

How much is enough?

As scientists learn more about the effects of sugar on the body, the recommendations change. For many years, the advice was to limit added sugars to 10% or lower of your calorie intake. This works out at about 70 grams (2 ½ oz) per day for men and 50 grams (1 ⅘ oz) per day for women, though it varies depending on your weight and how active you are.

To put it into perspective, one teaspoon of sugar is about 4 grams (⅕ oz), so the average woman is generally recommended to have no more than 12 teaspoons of sugar a day. That may sound like a lot, but a regular-sized can of soft drink has about nine teaspoons of sugar and some chocolate bars have in excess of eight teaspoons. Add a yogurt or a bowl of breakfast cereal and you can use up your daily allowance before you know it.

Going lower

In recent years, the World Health Organization (WHO) has published new recommendations calling for adults to cut their sugar intake in half, to about six teaspoons a day. To achieve this, you will have to be really smart about what you eat. Natural sugars, such as those found in fruit, are not included in the six teaspoons but many types of processed food have added sugar. For example, one tablespoon of tomato ketchup can contain one teaspoon of sugar.

TAKING THE RIGHT STEPS

To cut added sugars from your diet, you will have to be disciplined. Reading food labels carefully can help you to keep a track of your sugar intake. Reducing your intake of processed foods is another key step. If you aim to make meals yourself from fresh ingredients, you will know exactly what goes in them.

Going sugar-free

Cutting sugar from your diet won't always be easy, but people all over the world are already seeing the benefits of reduced sugar intake – and you can join them.

KEEP A DIARY

You may think that your sugar intake is fairly low, but most of us eat more sugar than we realise. Keep a detailed food diary for a few days, recording everything you eat and drink. Check labels carefully to work out your total sugar intake. That will give you a good starting point for setting targets when you start to go sugar-free.

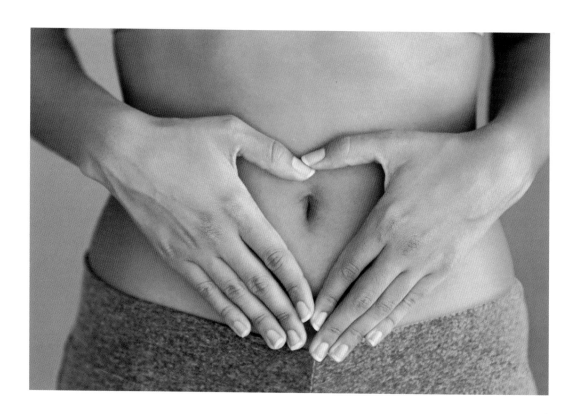

How low can you go?

If you search online, you will find various approaches to going sugar-free. Many people focus on eliminating added sugar from their diet. Others take it a step further and eliminate all foods containing sugar, even natural sugars such as those found in fruit. How far you want to go is up to you. Your body doesn't need sugar, so it won't be harmed by eliminating it completely. However, fruits have a lot of other nutrients that are good for you. Most doctors recommend limiting the amount of fruit you eat, but not cutting it out entirely. Therefore, most people who want a sugar-free diet will tend to cut refined sugar out of their diets, but will still eat honey and other naturally occurring sugars and sweeteners. The following recipes in this book will help you cut out refined sugars while incorporating sugar substitutes and natural sweeteners, such as honey.

Cutting sugar out of your diet is a challenge, but it does not have to be an all-or-nothing exercise. If you reduce your sugar intake slowly, while allowing yourself a few occasional treats, you will still feel some of the health benefits. Once you start cutting out sugar, you will soon get used to it and be able to cut out even more.

Take it slow

If you are used to having sugar in your diet, cutting it out entirely will be a shock to the system. You might manage a few days of the new regime and then give up because you are craving sugar. It is much more effective to reduce your sugar intake gradually, over a few weeks or months. This gives your body a chance to adjust to the new diet. For example, you can start by reducing the amount of sugar you put in tea or coffee or cut down on the number of fizzy drinks you have. Once that feels 'normal', you can reduce your sugar intake further.

You may feel tired at first when you start cutting out sugar. Some people experience headaches and cravings for sweet things. Make sure you are eating a healthy, balanced diet and try snacking on fruits, such as strawberries and apples, to fend off sugar cravings. Soon, your body will be used to it and you will feel great.

Feeling good

Once you are used to having less sugar, you will start to feel – and see – changes in your body. Many people who go sugar-free report that they feel less hungry and have more energy. This is because your body uses up sugar quickly but energy from other sources, such as vegetables, is much longer-lasting. You will probably start to lose weight.

KEEP IT SIMPLE

At first, going sugar-free will take up time. You will be spending more time reading labels, planning meals and trying new recipes. If you try to do it at the same time as taking on a big project at work, or planning a wedding, for example, you might feel overwhelmed. Choose a time when you can focus on your diet without too many distractions. Once you are into the swing of it, things will go back to normal.

Reading food labels

Sometimes it is not obvious how much sugar a particular food contains. If you want to cut out sugar, you will need to read nutrition labels carefully. Have a look at the labels on the foods in your cupboards and your fridge – you will probably be amazed at how much sugar some of them have. After a while, you will get used to buying particular low-sugar ingredients or varieties of foods that do not contain refined sugar.

What to look for

Nutrition labels show the amount of sugar per 100 grams (3 ½ oz) of food, which makes it easy to compare different foods. Find the figure for 'carbohydrates (of which sugars)' on the label. If the figure is more than 22.5 grams (¾ oz) of total sugars per 100 grams (3 ½ oz), that is considered to be a high amount of sugar. Anything with 5 grams or fewer per 100 grams (3 ½ oz) is low sugar.

These figures include natural sugars, such as those found in fruit and milk, as well as added sugars. If you have two foods that have the same total amount of sugar, but one is higher in milk and/or fruit content, this will be a better choice because you will be eating naturally occuring sugars.

Traffic lights

Some foods have useful labels on the front of the packaging that show you, at a glance, whether they are high in sugar. They usually use a traffic-light system: red for high sugar, amber for medium and green for low. If you're rushing to finish your shop and don't have time to read the ingredients lists, ditch the foods with red sugar content and make sure that your basket is filled with green ones instead.

It doesn't take an expert to realise that foods such as sweets, biscuits, cakes and chocolate have a lot of sugar. However, many other packaged foods can have surprisingly high amounts of added sugar too. Reading labels carefully will help you cut out added sugars from your diet.

SUGAR BY A DIFFERENT NAME

All packaged foods are required to list their ingredients by order of weight, so the first names on the list make up the bulk of the food. Added sugars can sometimes be camouflaged when they appear in ingredients lists. Here are some other terms you might see: sucrose, glucose, maltose, barley malt, hydrolysed starch, invert sugar, fruit juice concentrate, corn syrup. These are all types of added sugar. If you find them near the top of the ingredients list, stay away.

what not to eat

Steering clear of chocolate breakfast cereals is a no-brainer, but even some of the seemingly healthier brands can have a lot of added sugar. Don't be fooled by packets that say 'reduced sugar', 'enriched' or 'wholegrain' – these labels can make a product look healthy but the nutrition label will tell you the truth. Some foods that are advertised as 'fat-free' (such as yogurts) often have a lot of sugar added to make up for the flavour lost when fat is removed.

MAKE YOUR OWN

Have you ever made your own pasta sauce? Now is a great time to start! Jars of pasta sauce often contain a lot of added sugar but, if you make your own, you will know it is sugar-free. It is easier than you might think, and you can make a big batch and freeze portions for another day. It will also taste fresher and be more flavoursome.

Drinks

Fizzy drinks are one of the biggest no-nos if you want to go sugar-free. A single can of soft drink can contain more than half the recommended daily limit. Diet soft drinks are lower in sugar but have no real nutritional value. If you cannot survive without fizzy drinks, try diluting unsweetened fruit juice with sparkling water. But watch out for juice drinks that are sweetened with added sugar!

Alcoholic drinks contain sugar but some are better than others. For example, a dry red wine has less sugar than white wine. You should avoid champagne and sweet dessert wines. Spirits such as gin, vodka and whisky are low in sugar, but be careful of mixers – they are usually full of sugar. Stick to soda water, diet or slimline mixers.

Low-sugar stars

It is easy to look at a list of high-sugar foods and wonder what is left that is 'safe' to eat. Luckily, there is a huge range of low-sugar foods available. Even a picky eater will find plenty of healthy foods to choose from.

Meat and fish

Lean meats and fish are a great low-sugar option because they are packed with protein and other nutrients. Watch out for sugar-cured meats, such as some types of ham, and sauces or marinades that might be high in sugar. Eggs, beans and unsalted nuts are also good sources of low-sugar protein.

Go green

Vegetables are one of the best options
for a sugar-free diet because most
are low in natural sugars. A few to
watch out for are beetroot, carrot
and parsnip, which contain a higher
amount of natural sugar. You can still
eat them, just in moderation. Broccoli,
asparagus, beans and sweet potatoes
are full of nutrients and low in sugar.

Grains

Carbohydrates are found in grains
such as wheat. Your body turns
carbohydrates into sugars, so many
people on a sugar-free diet try to limit
the carbohydrates they consume.
As a general rule, stay away from
refined white flour and foods made
from it, such as white bread and
pasta. Other grains, such as oats
and brown rice, are much healthier.
When choosing bread products, look
out for 'wholegrain' on the label and
make sure to check for added sugar.

BREAKFAST

When it comes to breakfast, plain porridge is a low-sugar winner. But, if you
prefer toast, you can still eat it. Make sure to choose wholegrain bread and replace
jam or chocolate spreads with cream cheese.

Fruit: friend or foe?

One of the main topics of debate among people going sugar-free is whether or not to eat fruit. Fruit contains fructose (a type of natural sugar) so many people eliminate it from their diets along with refined and added sugars. However, it is not so simple. Unlike refined sugar, fruits contain a lot of useful nutrients including fibre, vitamin C, folic acid and potassium.

Many doctors and nutritionists recommend keeping fruit in your diet but limiting the quantity you eat – two pieces a day is a common guideline. Vegetables have many of the same nutrients as fruits but fewer calories and less sugar, so replace fruits with vegetables wherever you can. When you eat fruit, make sure it is as low-sugar as possible. For example, choose tins of fruit in juice rather than in syrup.

Instead of...	Eat
Grapes	Raspberries
Apple	Pear
Banana	Kiwi fruit
Cherries	Cranberries
Watermelon	Blueberries

The best fruits

In nutritional terms, no two fruits are alike. Some have more fructose and fibre than others. As a general rule, you should avoid fruits that have a high fructose content but little fibre, and try to eat those with high fibre and low fructose.

NO JUICE!

Sugars in fruits are less likely to cause tooth decay because of the way the sugars are contained within the structure of the fruit. When fruit is turned into juice, the sugars are released, so it's best to cut out fruit juice and stick to eating whole fruit and drinking water instead.

Eating out

Eating a meal at a restaurant with friends is one of life's great joys, but you don't always know exactly what goes into the food. How can you stick to a sugar-free diet while eating out? It definitely takes more willpower than eating at home. Here are a few tips to help you:

- Arrive with a positive mindset – be excited about what you can eat rather than focusing on what you can't.

- Order a starter and a main meal rather than a main meal and a dessert, as desserts are often packed with refined sugars.

- Stick to fish, meat and vegetables when choosing your food.

- Go easy on condiments and salad dressings – these often have a lot of sugar. A plain vinaigrette dressing is usually low in sugar, but balsamic vinegar is high is sugar.

- Avoid dishes with tomato-based or fruity sauces, as these often contain sugars.

- Ask the waiter about the menu – because many people are choosing to go sugar-free, restaurants are used to being asked which dishes are lowest in sugar.

- Don't be afraid to order your food exactly as you want it. For example, if there is a sauce that might be sugary, ask to have it left off your plate.

- Go for sparkling water, rather than a fizzy drink. If you want alcohol, choose a small glass of dry red wine.

- If your friends try to tempt you into eating a sugary treat, be firm and explain how much better you are feeling as a result of your new diet.

BE PREPARED

If you are going to eat out, you might be able to plan ahead. Some restaurants have nutritional information for their menus posted on their websites. Have a look before you go out and choose an option that is sugar-free, or at least low in sugar.

Being active, staying safe

Going sugar-free is just one part of a new, healthier lifestyle. If you seriously reduce your sugar intake, you will probably lose weight and, if you increase the amount of exercise you do, then you will lose even more. Being active does not have to mean joining a gym or doing a sport you hate – even small changes in your daily routine can have a positive impact.

You don't have to break a sweat to get the benefit from exercise. It's all about keeping moving throughout the day and you can work it into things you already do. Instead of using the lift, take the stairs. Walk about while you talk on the phone. Get off the bus two or three stops earlier and walk the rest of the way. If you are driving to the shops, park a bit further away than usual. Little things like this can really add up!

If you are ready to step it up a bit, jogging, cycling and swimming are great ways to burn calories. Don't worry if you are stuck indoors – put on some music and dance around the house or give the housework some extra oomph!

Feel the benefits

Keeping active is great for your health. It helps keep your heart healthy, reduces your risk of serious illness and strengthens muscles and bones. It can make you lose weight more quickly and often leaves you feeling more energetic.

WORKING TOGETHER

Find a friend who is also trying to be more active. If you have someone to exercise with, you'll be more motivated to keep it up. Taking a short walk at lunch with a work colleague will burn calories – and it's a great excuse for a chat, too!

Is it safe?

Going sugar-free is just like any other major lifestyle change – you should make sure you are ready for it. Even if you are in good health, it's best to talk to your doctor before you start. Your doctor can make sure your body can cope with a change in diet and maybe even provide some useful tips!

It is especially important to talk to your doctor if you are pregnant or trying to become pregnant, if you have a history of eating disorders or if you have any other health concerns. Your doctor might want to do a blood test for diabetes before you start, especially if you have a history of it in your family.

Ready to go

Before you start, have a look through your kitchen and get rid of anything that is going to tempt you. So often we eat things just because they are there – not because we are particularly hungry. If your cupboards are full of biscuits, it is going to be hard to stick to a sugar-free diet. Make a fresh start by filling your cupboards and fridge with healthy snacks, such as nuts and carrot sticks.

Tell your friends and family about your new regime. If they know what you are doing, they can offer help and support – and they might even want to join in! Any kind of lifestyle change is easier if you're not doing it alone.

KEEP TRACK

Before you start your sugar-free diet, step on the scales and take a photo of yourself so that, if you're going sugar-free for weight loss purposes, you can make comparisons once you lose weight. Make a note of your measurements – sometimes it can feel like the weight loss is slow, but you'll probably be losing centimetres.

Keeping motivated

Sticking to any kind of new routine is easiest if you have a clear idea of why you are doing it. You also have to know what you want to get out of it. Sit down and make a list of your reasons for going sugar-free. Keep your list to hand so that you can look at it any time you feel like you can't do it. Reminding yourself of all those health benefits can give you the motivation to keep going.

Make a plan

Think about how you want to cut down your sugar intake. If you are doing it gradually, write down a plan to show your targets, week by week. You might even choose some low-sugar recipes to try each week. It is easy to get so busy that you just want to make things easier by going back to your old routine. If you already have a plan in place, you'll be more likely to stick with it.

Setting goals

What do you hope to get out of going sugar-free? Most people want to improve their health and lose weight. Think about your short-term and long-term goals. Set yourself a realistic target weight and make a plan for how to get there.

Reward yourself

Set up a star chart for yourself. It works for children, so why not for you? Every day that you stick to your sugar limits, give yourself a star. Once you have enough stars (a whole week's worth, for example) you can reward yourself with a prize, such as a magazine or a new item of clothing.

SUPPORT FROM FRIENDS

Share your plans and goals with a close friend. They can help you keep track of your progress and offer encouragement and support – as well as a big hug when you reach your goals!

Breakfasts and brunches

Breakfasts and mid-morning meals can be packed with refined sugar. Even cereals and muesli that you may presume to be a healthy option can sometimes contain a lot of added sugar, which is why it is important to take the time to check the label and ingredients of food products.

Sugar-free breakfasts and brunches – once you know how – can be healthy, sugar-free and just as tasty. Considered by many as the most important meal of the day, breakfast should be nutritious and filling – in turn, this will fuel your body with long-lasting energy and should stop you feeling the urge to snack on sugary treats.

The following chapter contains delicious recipes that are free of refined sugar. The Blueberry Smoothie Bowl will give you the vitamins your body loves or the refreshing Summer Berry Waffles will give you a hit of sweetness without the refined sugar. If you prefer something more traditional, the Banana and Strawberry Porridge is a great option, which will keep you feeling fuller for longer.

Preparation time: **15 minutes**

Cooking time: **15 minutes**

Banana and honey pancakes

250 g / 9 oz / 1 ²/₃ cups plain
(all-purpose) flour

2 tsp baking powder

4 very ripe bananas

2 large eggs

225 ml / 8 fl. oz / ¾ cups whole milk

2 tbsp butter

manuka honey, to serve

1. Mix the flour and baking powder in a bowl
   and make a well in the centre.

2. Mash two of the bananas with a fork until
   smooth, then whisk in the eggs and milk.
   Gradually whisk the mixture into the
   flour bowl.

3. Melt the butter in a frying pan then whisk it
   into the batter. Put the buttered frying pan
   back over a low heat.

4. Spoon heaped tablespoons of the batter
   into the pan and cook for 2 minutes or until
   small bubbles start to appear on the surface.
   Turn the pancakes over with a spatula and
   cook the other side until golden brown
   and cooked through.

5. Repeat until all the batter has been used,
   keeping the finished batches warm in a
   low oven.

6. Stack the pancakes on warm plates. Slice the
   other two bananas and arrange on top, then
   serve with manuka honey for drizzling.

SERVES: 2

Preparation time: **25 minutes**

Blueberry smoothie bowl

50 g / 1 ¾ oz / ¼ cup chia seeds

250 ml / 9 fl. oz / 1 cup unsweetened
    acai berry juice

250 ml / 9 fl. oz / 1 cup unsweetened
    soya milk

150 g / 5 ½ oz / 1 cup frozen blueberries

2 tbsp manuka honey

TO GARNISH

2 tbsp chia seeds

2 tbsp fennel pollen

1. Stir the chia seeds into the acai juice and soya
   milk and leave to thicken for 20 minutes.

2. Transfer to a liquidizer and add the frozen
   blueberries and manuka honey.

3. Blend until very smooth, then divide between
   two bowls. Sprinkle with chia seeds and
   fennel pollen and serve immediately.

S E R V E S : 2

Preparation time: **10 minutes**

Cooking time: **5 minutes**

Ultimate bacon sandwich

6 rashers back bacon

4 slices wholemeal sourdough bread

1 ripe avocado, peeled and stoned

½ lime, juiced

2 tomatoes, diced

1 handful basil leaves, chopped

1 handful mustard cress

4 lettuce leaves

125 g / 4 ½ oz / 1 ball buffalo
mozzarella, sliced

1. Dry-fry the bacon in a non-stick frying pan for 2 minutes on each side.

2. Meanwhile, toast the bread on one side under a hot grill.

3. Mash the avocado with the lime juice and season with salt and pepper. Spread the untoasted side of the bread with avocado.

4. Mix the tomatoes with the basil and mustard cress and spoon two thirds of the mixture over two slices of the bread. Top with lettuce, followed by the bacon and mozzarella.

5. Spoon the rest of the tomato mixture on top, then close the sandwiches with the other two slices of bread.

6. Cut in half and serve immediately.

SERVES : 1

Preparation time: **5 minutes**

Cooking time: **15 minutes**

Breakfast bake

200 g / 7 oz / ¾ cup canned tomatoes, chopped

1 pinch chilli (chili) flakes

½ clove garlic, crushed

3 rashers smoked bacon, sliced

2 large eggs

1 tbsp flat-leaf parsley, chopped

1. Preheat the oven to 180°C (160°C fan) / 350F / gas 4.
2. Stir the tomatoes, chilli flakes and garlic together in a round baking tin and season with salt and pepper.
3. Stir in the bacon, then make two hollows in the mixture and break in the eggs.
4. Transfer to the oven and bake for 15 minutes or until the tomatoes are bubbling and the egg whites have set.
5. Serve immediately, garnished with parsley.

SERVES : 2

Preparation time: **10 minutes**

Freezing time: **2 hours**

chocolate almond smoothie bowl

3 bananas, sliced

600 ml / 1 pint / 2 ½ cups almond milk

2 tbsp unsweetened almond butter

1 tbsp unsweetened cocoa powder

2 tbsp manuka honey

2 tbsp natural yogurt

50 g / 1 ¾ oz / ⅓ cup sugar-free dark
   chocolate, broken into squares

5 strawberries, halved

2 tbsp fresh pomegranate seeds

1. Spread the banana slices out on a baking tray
   and freeze for at least 2 hours. They can then
   be stored in a freezer bag for later use or
   used straight away.

2. Put the frozen banana in a liquidizer with the
   almond milk, almond butter, cocoa powder
   and honey and blend until very smooth.

3. Pour into two bowls and swirl a little yogurt
   into each one.

4. Grate one of the squares of chocolate over
   the top of the bowls, then garnish with the
   rest of the chocolate, the strawberries and
   pomegranate seeds.

5. Serve immediately.

SERVES: 2

Preparation time: **35 minutes**

Two-tone chia smoothie

2 tbsp chia seeds

100 ml / 3 ½ fl. oz / ½ cup orange juice,
    freshly squeezed

100 ml / 3 ½ fl. oz / ½ cup unsweetened
    pomegranate juice

2 tbsp goji berries

150 g / 5 ½ oz / 1 cup strawberries, hulled
    and halved

8 ice cubes

1 ripe mango, peeled, stoned and chopped

1. Stir 1 tablespoon of chia seeds into the orange
   juice and set aside. Stir the rest of the chia
   seeds into the pomegranate juice with the
   goji berries and leave to soak for **30 minutes**.

2. Transfer the pomegranate mixture to a
   liquidizer and add the strawberries and
   half the ice cubes. Blend until very smooth,
   then divide between two glass bottles.

3. Rinse out the liquidizer, then add the orange
   mixture, mango and the rest of the ice cubes.
   Blend until very smooth, then top up the
   smoothie bottles and serve immediately.

SERVES: 4

Preparation time: **10 minutes**

Cooking time: **25 minutes**

Summer berry waffles

250 g / 9 oz / 1 ²/₃ cups plain (all-purpose) flour

2 tsp baking powder

2 large eggs

300 ml / 10 ½ fl. oz / 1 ¼ cups whole milk

2 tbsp butter, melted

sunflower oil, for oiling the waffle maker

300 g / 10 ½ oz / 2 cups mixed summer berries, to serve

1. Put the oven on a low setting and put an electric waffle maker on to heat.

2. Mix the flour and baking powder in a bowl and make a well in the centre.

3. Break in the eggs and pour in the milk then use a whisk to gradually incorporate all of the flour from around the outside, followed by the melted butter.

4. Spoon some of the batter into the waffle maker and close the lid. Cook for 4 minutes, or according to the manufacturer's instructions, until golden brown.

5. Repeat until all the batter has been used, keeping the finished batches warm in the oven.

6. Serve the waffles as soon as possible, scattered with berries.

SERVES: 4

Preparation time: **15 minutes**

Cooking time: **20 minutes**

Red velvet crepes

150 g / 5 ½ oz / 1 cup plain
  (all-purpose) flour

1 tbsp unsweetened cocoa powder

1 large egg

325 ml / 11 ½ fl. oz / 1 ⅓ cups whole milk

½ tsp red food colouring

1 tbsp butter

100 g / 3 ½ oz / ⅔ cup raspberries

100 g / 3 ½ oz / ⅔ cup blueberries

single (light) cream, to serve

1. Sieve the flour and cocoa into a bowl and make a well in the centre. Break in the egg and pour in the milk and food colouring, then use a whisk to gradually incorporate all of the flour from around the outside.

2. Melt the butter in a medium frying pan then whisk it into the batter.

3. Put the buttered frying pan back over a low heat. Add a small ladle of batter and swirl the pan to coat the bottom.

4. When it starts to dry and curl up at the edges, turn the crepe over with a spatula and cook the other side until golden brown and cooked through. Repeat with the rest of the mixture, keeping the finished crepes warm in a low oven.

5. Fold the crepes in half and layer several on four plates. Serve scattered with berries and drizzled with single cream.

SERVES : 2

Preparation time: **5 minutes**

Cooking time: **25 minutes**

Griddled full English breakfast

4 good quality pork sausages

2 tbsp sunflower oil

4 portobello mushrooms

3 tomatoes, halved

4 rashers back bacon

2 large eggs

125 g / 4 ½ oz / ½ cup no-added sugar
   baked beans

flat-leaf parsley, to garnish

1. Brush the sausages with 1 teaspoon of the oil
   and fry in a griddle pan for 15 minutes,
   turning occasionally. Transfer the sausages
   to a plate and keep warm in a low oven.

2. Brush the mushrooms with 2 teaspoons of oil
   and season. Cook gill-side-down for
   3 minutes. Brush the cut side of the tomatoes
   with 1 teaspoon of oil and season with salt
   and pepper. Turn the mushrooms over and
   add the tomatoes cut-side-down. Griddle for
   4 minutes, then transfer to the sausage plate.

3. Griddle the bacon for 2 minutes on each side.

4. Meanwhile, heat the remaining 2 teaspoons
   of oil in a frying pan and fry the eggs to
   your liking.

5. While the eggs are cooking, heat the baked
   beans in a saucepan or microwave according
   to the manufacturer's instructions.

6. Divide all the components between two warm
   plates and serve, garnished with parsley.

SERVES: 2

Preparation time: **25 minutes**

Acai chia smoothie bowl

50 g / 1 ¾ oz / ¼ cup chia seeds

28 g / 1 oz / ¼ cup buckwheat
  porridge flakes

250 ml / 9 fl. oz / 1 cup unsweetened acai
  berry juice

250 ml / 9 fl. oz / 1 cup unsweetened
  almond milk

150 g / 5 ½ oz / 1 cup frozen summer berries

2 tbsp manuka honey

TO GARNISH

1 handful fresh berries, sliced if large

2 tbsp goji berries

2 tbsp chia seeds

2 tbsp fennel pollen

1. Stir the chia seeds and buckwheat flakes into the acai juice and almond milk and leave to thicken for 20 minutes.

2. Transfer to a liquidizer and add the frozen berries and manuka honey.

3. Blend until very smooth, then divide between two bowls.

4. Arrange the berries on top and sprinkle with chia seeds and fennel pollen.

5. Serve immediately.

SERVES: 4

Preparation time: **5 minutes**

Cooking time: **8 minutes**

Banana and strawberry porridge

2 large ripe bananas

600 ml / 1 pint / 2 ½ cups whole milk,
  plus extra to serve

125 g / 4 ½ oz / 1 ¼ cups rolled
  porridge oats

2 tbsp manuka honey

100 g / 3 ½ oz / ⅔ cup strawberries, hulled
  and quartered

1. Mash one of the bananas and mix it with
   the milk and oats in a saucepan. Stir over
   a medium heat until it starts to simmer.

2. Add the manuka honey and a pinch of salt,
   then reduce the heat to its lowest setting
   and continue to stir for 5 minutes.

3. Divide the porridge between four bowls.
   Slice the other banana and arrange on top
   with the strawberries. Serve immediately
   with extra milk to pour over at the table.

SERVES: 2

Preparation time: **35 minutes**

Berry smoothie bowl

28 g / 1 oz / ¼ cup rolled porridge oats

250 ml / 9 fl. oz / 1 cup unsweetened
  pomegranate juice

150 g / 5 ½ oz / 1 cup frozen blueberries

2 tbsp manuka honey

250 ml / 9 fl. oz / 1 cup Greek yogurt

TO GARNISH

28 g / 1 oz / ¼ cup unsweetened granola

75 g / 2 ½ oz / ½ cup fresh blueberries

50 g / 1 ¾ oz / ⅓ cup fresh
  pomegranate seeds

2 tbsp unsweetened desiccated coconut

1. Stir the oats into the pomegranate juice
   and leave to soak for 30 minutes.

2. Transfer to a liquidizer and add the
   frozen blueberries, manuka honey and
   all but 2 tablespoons of the yogurt.

3. Blend until very smooth, then pour into
   two bowls.

4. Swirl the rest of the yogurt into the
   smoothies, then scatter over the granola and
   top with fresh blueberries and pomegranate
   seeds. Sprinkle with coconut and serve
   immediately.

Lunches and light bites

When you're pushed for time midday, it is easy to grab a sandwich, crisps and a chocolate bar. Instead, make the effort to eat something healthy. Omelettes and risottos are perfect at banishing that lunchtime lull. Alternatively, if you prefer to pack lunch to take with you, wraps are ideal to eat on the go.

Soup is a great option for a healthy, sugar-free lunch. Beware of shop-bought soups – some have a lot of salt and added sugar, so be sure to check the label or try making your own! If you make a big batch and freeze the soup in individual portions, you will not only cut costs but also have convenient, ready-made lunches for several days.

Salads are another great sugar-free choice for lunch or as a light bite. Make sure you don't undo all your good work by slathering on a sugar-laden dressing. Instead, make your own by mixing olive oil and lemon juice.

The following lunches and light bites recipes will help you steer clear of refined sugar and will inspire you to eat healthily. From soups and salads to fritters and vegetable quiche, there are lots of dishes to try out.

MAKES : 1

Preparation time: **10 minutes**

Cooking time: **5 minutes**

Spinach omelette

25 g / 1 oz / ¾ cup baby leaf spinach

2 tbsp cress, plus extra to garnish

2 tbsp basil leaves, chopped

2 tbsp milk

2 large eggs

½ tbsp butter

⅓ yellow pepper, sliced

5 cherry tomatoes, quartered

50 g / 1 ¾ oz / ½ cup goat's cheese, crumbled

tomatoes, peanuts and olives, to serve

1. Put the spinach, cress, basil, milk and eggs in a liquidizer. Blend until smooth.

2. Heat the butter in a non-stick frying pan until sizzling, then pour in the egg mixture.

3. Cook over a medium heat until the eggs start to set around the outside. Use a spatula to draw the sides of the omelette into the centre and tilt the pan to fill the gaps with more liquid egg.

4. Repeat the process until the top of the omelette is just set, then scatter over the pepper, tomatoes and goat's cheese.

5. Fold the omelette in half, slide it onto a plate and scatter with more cress. Serve with tomatoes, peanuts and olives.

SERVES: 2

Preparation time: **15 minutes**

Cooking time: **35 minutes**

Risotto with spinach and garlic

2 tbsp olive oil

1 onion, finely chopped

2 cloves of garlic, finely chopped

100 g / 3 ½ oz / 3 cups spinach

¼ tsp nutmeg, finely grated

750 litre / 1 pint 5 ½ fl. oz / 3 cups good
   quality vegetable stock

150 g / 5 ½ oz / ¾ cup risotto rice

250 ml / 9 fl. oz / 1 cup dry white wine

50 g / 1 ¾ oz / ½ cup Parmesan, finely grated

2 tbsp butter

1. Heat the oil in a sauté pan and fry the onion
   for 10 minutes without colouring. Add the garlic
   and cook for 2 minutes then add the spinach.
   Cover with a lid and steam until it has wilted
   right down. Stir well and season with nutmeg,
   salt and pepper.

2. Transfer the spinach to a liquidizer with the stock
   and blend until smooth. Pour the mixture into a
   saucepan and bring to a simmer.

3. Tip the rice into the sauté pan and toast over
   a medium heat for 1 minute. Add the wine and
   cook until almost evaporated.

4. Add two ladles of the hot spinach stock, then
   cook, stirring occasionally, until most of the
   stock has been absorbed before adding the next
   two ladles. Continue in this way for around
   20 minutes or until the rice is just tender.

5. Stir in the Parmesan and butter, then season
   to taste with salt and pepper.

6. Cover the pan and leave to rest off the heat for
   4 minutes before serving.

SERVES: 4

Preparation time: **15 minutes**

Cooking time: **30 minutes**

Spiced butternut squash soup

2 tbsp olive oil

1 onion, finely chopped

2 cloves of garlic, finely chopped

1 tsp ground cumin

½ tsp ground coriander

1 large butternut squash, peeled, deseeded
and cut into chunks

1 litre / 1 pint 15 fl. oz / 4 cups
vegetable stock

2 tsp smoked paprika

2 tbsp flax seeds

75 ml / 2 ½ fl. oz / ⅓ cup mascarpone

1. Heat the oil in a large saucepan and fry
   the onion and garlic for 10 minutes to soften
   without colouring.

2. Add the cumin, coriander and squash to the
   pan and stir to coat in the oil, then pour in
   the stock and bring to the boil. Reduce the
   heat a little and simmer for 20 minutes or
   until the squash is tender.

3. Blend the soup until smooth, using a
   liquidizer or immersion blender, then taste
   and adjust the seasoning.

4. Ladle the soup into warm bowls and sprinkle
   with smoked paprika and flax seeds.

5. Serve with a bowl of mascarpone on the side
   for stirring in at the table.

SERVES: 4

Preparation time: **40 minutes**

Chilling time: **1 hour**

Cooking time: **15 minutes**

Spiced lamb koftas

75 g / 2 ½ oz / ⅓ cup red lentils

6 spring onions, roughly chopped

1 clove of garlic, crushed

1 tsp chilli (chili) flakes)

1 tsp ground cumin

1 tsp ground coriander

½ tsp ground mixed spice

1 tsp dried oregano

450 g / 1 lb / 3 cups minced lamb

1. Cook the lentils in boiling water for 20 minutes, then drain well and leave to cool.

2. Meanwhile, put four wooden skewers in a bowl of water and leave to soak for 20 minutes.

3. Put the lentils in a food processor with the rest of the ingredients and a big pinch of salt and pepper. Pulse until finely chopped and evenly mixed.

4. Divide the kofta mixture into four pieces and shape them around the skewers. Chill in the fridge for 1 hour or until firm.

5. Cook the koftas over a charcoal barbecue or under a hot grill for 15 minutes, turning occasionally, until cooked through.

SERVES: 4

Preparation time: **25 minutes**

Cooking time: **4 minutes**

Courgette fritters

3 medium courgettes (zucchini)

50 g / 1 ¾ oz / ⅓ cup plain
   (all-purpose) flour

1 tbsp cornflour (cornstarch)

½ tsp baking powder

2 large eggs, separated

1 lemon, zest finely grated

2 spring onions (scallions), finely chopped

2 tbsp flat-leaf parsley, chopped, plus a few
   sprigs to garnish

2 tbsp basil leaves, shredded

2 tbsp olive oil

Greek yogurt, for dipping

1. Coarsely grate the courgettes into the centre of
   a clean tea towel, then gather up the edges and
   twist to squeeze out as much liquid as possible.

2. Mix the flour, cornflour and baking powder in a
   bowl. Stir 60 ml of cold water into the egg yolks
   with the lemon zest and a big pinch of salt and
   pepper, then whisk the mixture into the flour to
   form a thick batter. Fold the courgette, spring
   onions and herbs into the batter.

3. Whisk the egg whites until stiff in a clean bowl,
   then fold them in to lighten the mixture.

4. Heat the oil in a frying pan and fry heaped
   tablespoons of the mixture for 2 minutes on
   each side or until golden brown and cooked
   through.

5. Repeat until all of the mixture has been used,
   keeping the cooked fritters warm in a low oven.

6. Serve the fritters as soon as possible, with Greek
   yogurt for dipping. Garnish with parsley.

SERVES: 2-4

Preparation time: **5 minutes**

Cooking time: **15 minutes**

Creamy mushrooms

1 tbsp olive oil

1 tbsp butter

200 g / 7 oz / 2 ⅔ cups button
    mushrooms, sliced

1 tbsp fresh thyme, chopped, plus a few
    sprigs to garnish

2 cloves of garlic, crushed

75 ml / 2 ½ fl. oz / ⅓ cup dry white wine

250 ml / 9 fl. oz / 1 cup double
    (heavy) cream

1. Heat the oil and butter in a sauté pan and
    fry the mushrooms and thyme for 10 minutes
    or until any liquid from the mushrooms
    evaporates and they start to lightly colour.

2. Add the garlic and cook for 1 minute, stirring
    all the time, then add the wine and reduce
    by half.

3. Stir in the cream and simmer for 2 minutes
    or until it reaches your preferred consistency.

4. Season to taste with salt and pepper and
    serve as a light bite.

5. Alternatively, serve for lunch with pasta,
    chicken or steak.

SERVES: 4

Preparation time: **15 minutes**

Cooking time: **4 minutes**

Deep-fried mozzarella

50 g / 1 ¾ oz / ⅓ cup plain
   (all-purpose) flour

2 large eggs, beaten

100 g / 3 ½ oz / 1 cup panko breadcrumbs

375 g / 13 oz / 3 balls mozzarella quartered

sunflower oil, for deep-frying

tomato sauce, for dipping

basil leaves and tomatoes, to garnish

1. Put the flour, egg and panko breadcrumbs in three separate bowls.

2. Dip the mozzarella in the flour, then the egg, then the breadcrumbs, making sure it is well coated.

3. Heat the oil in a deep fat fryer, according to the manufacturer's instructions, to a temperature of 180°C (350F).

4. Lower the mozzarella into the fryer basket and cook for 4 minutes or until crisp and golden brown.

5. Drain on plenty of kitchen paper, then serve garnished with basil and tomatoes, with tomato sauce for dipping.

SERVES : 4

Preparation time: **10 minutes**

Marinating time: **1 hour**

Cooking time: **30 minutes**

Five-spice chicken legs

1 tbsp five-spice powder

2 cloves of garlic, crushed

1 tbsp fresh root ginger, finely grated

2 tbsp shaoxing rice wine

2 tbsp light soy sauce

1 tbsp sesame oil

2 tbsp manuka honey

8 chicken drumsticks

boiled new potatoes and salad, to serve

1. Whisk the five-spice, garlic and ginger into the rice wine, soy, sesame oil and honey. Pour the mixture into a freezer bag and add the chicken legs, then seal the bag and massage well to coat.

2. Leave to marinate in the fridge for at least 1 hour.

3. Preheat the oven to 200°C (180°C fan) / 400F / gas 6 and line a roasting tin with greaseproof paper.

4. Spread the chicken legs out in the roasting tin and roast for 30 minutes or until the juices run clear when the thickest part is pierced with a skewer.

5. Serve the chicken legs with new potatoes and salad.

SERVES : 4

Preparation time: **5 minutes**
Cooking time: **45 minutes**

French onion soup

2 tbsp olive oil

3 large onions, chopped

2 cloves of garlic, crushed

1 litre / 1 pint 14 fl. oz / 4 cups beef
  -or vegetable stock

⅓ stale baguette, cubed

75 g / 2 ½ oz / ¾ cup Gruyère, grated

1. Heat the oil in a saucepan then add the onions and stir well. Cover the pan and cook gently for 20 minutes, stirring occasionally. Add the garlic and cook uncovered for 5 more minutes, then stir in the stock and bring to the boil.

2. Simmer for 15 minutes then taste the soup and adjust the seasoning with salt and pepper.

3. When the soup is ready, divide it between four ovenproof bowls. Add the baguette cubes and top with the cheese.

4. Cook under the grill for 2 minutes or until golden and bubbling.

5. Serve immediately.

SERVES: 4

Preparation time: **10 minutes**

Cooking time: **30 minutes**

Roasted Vegetable Wraps

2 cloves of garlic, crushed

1 tsp ground cumin

½ tsp ground coriander

½ tsp cayenne pepper

50 ml / 1 ¾ fl. oz / ¼ cup olive oil

1 large courgette (zucchini), sliced

1 small cauliflower, broken into florets

4 soft flour tortillas (check the packet to
ensure there is no added sugar)

1 red pepper, deseeded and sliced

3 spring onions (scallions), chopped

1 handful coriander (cilantro) leaves

2 large ripe tomatoes

1. Preheat the oven to 200°C (180°C fan) /
   400F / gas 6.
2. Stir the garlic and spices into the oil and
   season with salt and pepper. Toss the spiced
   oil with the courgette and cauliflower and
   spread them out in a large roasting tin.
3. Roast for 30 minutes or until tender and
   golden brown, stirring halfway through.
4. Divide the vegetables between the tortillas
   and top with red pepper, spring onions
   and coriander.
5. Dice the tomatoes and serve in a bowl on
   the side for spooning over as a simple salsa
   at the table.

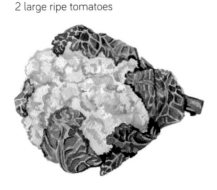

SERVES: 6

Preparation time: **1 hour**
Cooking time: **40 minutes**

Vegetable quiche

110 g / 4 oz / ½ cup butter, cubed and chilled

225 g / 8 oz / 1 ½ cups plain (all-purpose) flour

2 tbsp olive oil

6 spring onions (scallions), chopped

2 cloves of garlic, finely chopped

1 yellow pepper, deseeded and diced

1 green pepper, deseeded and diced

1 courgette (zucchini), diced

3 large eggs, beaten

225 ml / 8 fl. oz / ¾ cup double (heavy) cream

2 large tomatoes, peeled, deseeded and diced

75 g / 2 ½ oz / ½ cup Gruyère, grated

1. Rub the butter into the flour, then stir in just enough cold water to bring the pastry together into a pliable dough. Chill for 30 minutes.

2. Preheat the oven to 200°C (180°C fan) / 400F / gas 6.

3. Roll out the pastry and use it to line a 23 cm (9 in) pie dish. Prick it with a fork, line with clingfilm and fill with baking beans. Bake for 10 minutes, then remove the clingfilm and beans and cook for 5 minutes or until crisp.

4. Lower the temperature to 150°C (130°C fan) / 300F / gas 2. Heat the oil in a sauté pan and fry the leeks for 5 minutes. Add the garlic, peppers and courgette and sauté for 10 minutes.

5. Whisk the eggs with the double cream then stir in the vegetable mixture and tomatoes. Season generously with salt and pepper.

6. Pour the filling into the pastry case and scatter the cheese on top. Bake for 40 minutes or until just set in the centre.

SERVES: 4

Preparation time: **50 minutes**

Cooking time: **3 minutes**

Onion rings

2 medium onions, peeled

300 ml / 10 ½ fl. oz / 1 ¼ cups
    semi-skimmed milk

sunflower oil, for deep-frying

150 g / 3 ½ oz / 1 cup plain
    (all-purpose) flour

2 large eggs, beaten

150 g / 5 ½ oz / 1 cup fine dried
    breadcrumbs

FOR THE DIP

200 ml / 7 fl. oz / ¾ cup sour cream

2 tbsp chives, finely chopped

1 tbsp parsley, finely chopped

1. Thickly slice the onions, then separate the slices into rings. Soak the onion rings in milk for 30 minutes, then carefully remove the inner membrane from each ring. Drain well and pat dry with kitchen paper.

2. Meanwhile, make the dip by stirring all the ingredients together. Season to taste with salt and pepper.

3. Heat the oil in a deep fat fryer, according to the manufacturer's instructions, to a temperature of 180°C (350F).

4. Coat the onion rings in flour and shake off any excess. Dip them in egg, then roll in breadcrumbs to coat.

5. Fry the onion rings in batches for 3 minutes or until crisp and brown, then drain well and tip them into a kitchen paper lined bowl.

6. Serve immediately with the dip on the side.

SERVES: 4

Preparation time: **5 minutes**

Cooking time: **12 minutes**

Pasta salad

400 g / 14 oz / 4 cups dried fusilli pasta

½ head broccoli, cut into florets

150 g / 5 ½ oz / 1 cup frozen peas, defrosted

2 tbsp olive oil

2 tbsp fresh pesto

1 red pepper, deseeded and diced

2 avocados, peeled, stoned and diced

150 g / 5 ½ oz / 1 ½ cups goat's cheese, crumbled

1 handful basil leaves

1 lemon, cut into wedges

1. Boil the pasta in salted water according to the packet instructions.
2. 3 minutes before the pasta is due to be ready, add the broccoli and peas to the saucepan.
3. When the pasta and vegetables are cooked al dente, drain well, then plunge into iced water to stop the cooking. Drain well and toss with the oil and pesto.
4. Add the peppers, avocado, goat's cheese and basil to the salad and toss carefully to keep the ingredients intact.
5. Serve immediately or chill until you're ready to eat.
6. Garnish with lemon wedges for squeezing over at the table.

SERVES: 2

Preparation time: **20 minutes**

Cooking time: **10 minutes**

Quinoa tabbouleh

150 g / 5 ½ oz / ¾ cup mixed red and
white quinoa

150 ml / 5 ½ fl. oz / ²/₃ cup vegetable stock

1 lime, ½ juiced, half cut into wedges
to garnish

2 tbsp olive oil

¹/₃ cucumber, halved and thinly sliced

150 g / 5 ½ oz / 1 cup cherry
tomatoes, quartered

3 spring onions (scallions), chopped

1 large handful mizuna

1 large handful mixed baby salad leaves

1. Put the quinoa in a saucepan with the stock.
   Cover and simmer gently for 10 minutes,
   then leave to stand off the heat for a further
   15 minutes without lifting the lid.

2. Dress the quinoa with lime juice and olive oil
   and season to taste with salt and pepper.

3. Leave to cool to room temperature, then
   toss with the rest of the ingredients and
   serve immediately.

SERVES : 4

Preparation time: **10 minutes**

Cooking time: **30 minutes**

Sweet chilli kofta wraps

4 lamb koftas

4 soft flour tortillas (check the packet to ensure there is no added sugar)

1 carrot, coarsely grated

3 red cabbage leaves, shredded

¼ iceberg lettuce, sliced

50 ml / 1 ¾ fl. oz / ¼ cup no added sugar light mayonnaise

FOR THE SWEET CHILLI SAUCE

125 g / 4 ½ oz / 1 cup red chillies (chilies), deseeded and finely chopped

1 clove of garlic, crushed

175 ml / 6 fl. oz / ⅔ cup rice wine vinegar

125 ml / 4 ½ fl. oz / ½ cup raw honey

1. To make the sweet chilli sauce, put all the ingredients in a small saucepan. Stir over a medium heat until the mixture starts to simmer. Simmer without stirring for 15 minutes or until it thickens. Pour into a sterilised jar, screw on the lid and leave to cool to room temperature. Store in a cool dry place.

2. Cook the koftas over a charcoal barbecue or under a hot grill for 15 minutes, turning occasionally, until cooked through.

3. Top the tortillas with carrot, cabbage and lettuce, then arrange the koftas on top.

4. Drizzle the mayonnaise and sweet chilli sauce over the wraps. Serve immediately.

5. Once opened, the rest of the chilli sauce can be stored in the fridge for several weeks.

SERVES: 6

Preparation time: **5 minutes**

Cooking time: **3 hours 30 minutes**

Homemade baked beans

400 g / 14 oz / 2 ⅔ cups dried haricot
   beans, soaked overnight

75 ml / 2 ½ fl. oz / ⅓ cup olive oil

1 onion, finely chopped

2 cloves of garlic, crushed

½ tsp dried oregano

2 bay leaves

1 tbsp tomato puree

400 g / 14 oz / 1 ⅔ cups canned
   tomatoes, chopped

600 ml / 1 pint / 2 ½ cups vegetable stock

toasted baguette and cress, to serve

1. Drain the beans from their soaking water and
   put them in a large saucepan of cold water.
   Bring to the boil and cook for 10 minutes,
   then drain well.

2. Preheat the oven to 140°C (120°C fan) / 275F / gas 1.

3. Heat the oil in a cast iron casserole dish and fry
   the onion over a gentle heat for 15 minutes without
   colouring. Add the garlic, oregano and bay leaves
   and cook for 3 minutes, stirring regularly. Add
   the tomato puree and stir for 1 minute to cook
   out the raw flavour.

4. Stir in the canned tomatoes, vegetable stock
   and drained beans. If the liquid doesn't cover
   the beans by at least 2 cm, top it up with water.

5. When it starts to boil, cover the dish with a lid
   and transfer it to the oven. Bake for 3 hours or
   until the beans are tender, stirring occasionally.
   Season to taste with salt and pepper.

6. Serve the beans on toasted baguette with a
   sprinkling of cress.

SERVES: 2

Preparation time: **15 minutes**

Marinating time: **30 minutes**

Cooking time: **5 minutes**

Chicken and chickpea rice bowl

2 tbsp olive oil

2 tsp smoked paprika

1 tsp ground cumin

1 large skinless chicken breast, sliced
    diagonally

1 clove of garlic, crushed

250 g / 9 oz / 1 cup canned
    chickpeas, drained

steamed rice, to serve

$^1/_6$ red cabbage, shredded

1 red pepper, sliced

½ red onion, thinly sliced

1 avocado, peeled, stoned and sliced

1 handful mizuna

1 tbsp black sesame seeds

1. Mix 1 tablespoon of olive oil with 1 teaspoon of smoked paprika and $^1/_2$ tsp cumin. Season with salt and pepper, then brush it over the chicken and leave to marinate for 30 minutes.

2. Heat a griddle pan until smoking hot. Griddle the chicken for 2 minutes on each side or until cooked through.

3. Meanwhile, heat the rest of the oil in a small saucepan and fry the garlic for 1 minute. Add the drained chickpeas and the rest of the paprika and cumin. Add a splash of water, then cover and cook for 3 minutes or until piping hot.

4. Serve the chicken and chickpeas on steamed rice with the cabbage, pepper, red onion and avocado on the side.

5. Scatter with mizuna and sprinkle with sesame seeds. Serve immediately.

SERVES : 1

Preparation time: **5 minutes**

Cooking time: **15 minutes**

Mushroom and feta omelette

1 tbsp olive oil

50 g / 1 ¾ oz / ¼ cup butter

75 g / 2 ½ oz / 1 cup baby chestnut mushrooms

3 large eggs

1 avocado, peeled, stoned and cubed

75 g / 2 ½ oz / ¾ cup feta cheese, cubed

1 handful lettuce, chopped

2 tbsp flat leaf parsley, chopped

½ lemon, juiced

toasted baguette, to serve

1. Heat the olive oil and half the butter in a non-stick frying pan until sizzling. Add the mushrooms, season with salt and pepper and cook for 10 minutes, stirring occasionally. Transfer to a bowl and set aside.

2. Break the eggs into a jug with a pinch of salt and pepper and beat them gently to break up the yolks.

3. Add the rest of the butter to the frying pan and heat until sizzling, then pour in the eggs. Cook over a medium heat until the eggs start to set around the outside. Use a spatula to draw the sides of the omelette into the centre and tilt the pan to fill the gaps with more liquid egg. Repeat the process until the top of the omelette is just set then take off the heat.

4. Toss the mushrooms with the avocado, feta, lettuce and parsley and add a squeeze of lemon. Spoon the mixture on top of the omelette, then fold it in half and slide it onto a plate.

5. Serve with toasted baguette.

SERVES : 4

Preparation time: **10 minutes**

Cooking time: **25 minutes**

Creamy broccoli soup

1 tbsp olive oil

1 tbsp butter

1 leek, chopped

2 cloves of garlic, crushed

1 large head of broccoli, chopped

1.2 litres / 2 pints / 4 ¾ cups vegetable stock

1 bay leaf

200 ml / 7 fl. oz / ¾ cup crème fraiche

25 g / 1 oz / ¼ cup Parmesan, finely grated

1 tbsp balsamic vinegar

croutons, parsley and pumpkin seeds,
   to serve

1. Heat the oil and butter in a large saucepan
   and fry the leek and garlic over a low heat
   for 10 minutes. Add the broccoli, stock and
   bay leaf to the pan and bring to the boil.

2. Reduce the heat, then cover and simmer for
   10 minutes or until the broccoli is tender.

3. Remove the bay leaf and stir in half the crème
   fraiche. Blend until smooth with an immersion
   blender, then season to taste with salt
   and pepper.

4. Ladle the soup into four warm bowls and
   swirl some crème fraiche through the top of
   each one. Sprinkle with Parmesan and
   drizzle with balsamic vinegar, then garnish
   with croutons, parsley and pumpkin seeds.

SERVES: 6

Preparation time: **20 minutes**

Cooking time: **10 minutes**

Hot dogs with chimichurri

6 frankfurters (check the packet to ensure there is no dextrose)

6 seeded hotdog rolls (check the packet to ensure there is no added sugar)

pea shoots, to garnish

FOR THE CHIMICHURRI SAUCES

2 handfuls flat-leaf parsley leaves

1 handful mint leaves

1 handful oregano leaves

150 ml / 5 ½ fl. oz / ²/₃ cup olive oil

75 ml / 2 ½ fl. oz / ¹/₃ cup red wine vinegar

6 cloves of garlic, crushed

2 dried Chipotles, soaked in warm water for 20 minutes

100 g / 3 ½ oz / ½ cup roasted red peppers in oil, drained

1. First, make the green chimichurri. Put the parsley, mint and oregano in a liquidizer with half the oil, vinegar and garlic. Blend until smooth and season to taste with salt and pepper. Scrape the mixture into a bowl and rinse out the liquidizer.

2. To make the red chimichurri, put the rest of the oil, vinegar and garlic in the liquidizer with the chipotles and peppers. Blend until smooth, then season to taste and scrape into a bowl.

3. Cook the frankfurters according to the packet instructions on a barbecue or griddle pan.

4. Slice the frankfurters in half lengthways and serve in the hotdog rolls with the sauces spooned over.

5. Garnish with pea shoots.

Main meals

Main meals should be filling, healthy and most definitely delicious! The recipes in this chapter will inspire you to banish the sugar and keep the flavour. From Tuna Poke Bowl and Chicken Jambalaya to classic Chilli Con Carne or Bacon and Sweetcorn Pizza, there is something for everyone.

Fish is a fantastic choice for your main meal. It is sugar-free, high in protein and many types of fish are low in calories too. Not only that, but fish is very easy to cook and provides a great flavour. It can be cooked in many different ways and used in a variety of dishes such as burgers, savoury roulades and pasta.

Meat fits perfectly into a sugar-free diet. Stick to lean cuts and remove all visible fat and skin. Like other high-protein foods, meat can help you feel fuller for longer and supplies your body with vital minerals such as irons.

If you prefer to avoid meat and fish, this chapter also offers some vegetarian options. The Spanakopita or Pasta and Chickpea Salad are ideal for packing vitamin-rich vegetables into your diet.

Preparation time: **15 minutes**

Cooking time: **45 minutes**

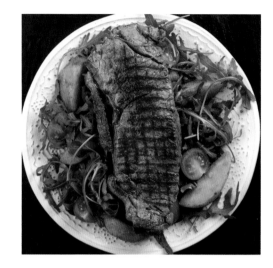

Steak and chips salad

800 g / 1 lb 12 oz King Edward potatoes, scrubbed and cut into wedges

1 tsp smoked paprika

1 tsp garlic powder

60 ml / 2 fl. oz / ¼ cup olive oil

4 sirloin steaks

300 g / 10 ½ oz / 2 cups cherry tomatoes, halved

100 g / 3 ½ oz / 3 cups rocket (arugula)

FOR THE DRESSING

½ tsp Dijon mustard

1 tsp manuka honey

½ lemon, juiced

2 tbsp olive oil

1. Preheat the oil in a large roasting tin in the oven at 200°C (180°C fan) / 400F / gas 6.

2. Parboil the potatoes in boiling salted water for 5 minutes, then drain well and leave to steam dry for 2 minutes.

3. Mix the paprika and garlic powder with ½ a teaspoon of salt and pepper and sprinkle it over the potatoes. Tip the wedges into the roasting tin and turn to coat in the oil. Bake for 45 minutes, turning every 15 minutes.

4. When the wedges have been in the oven for 25 minutes, heat two large griddle pans until smoking hot. Season the steaks liberally with salt and pepper and griddle for 8 minutes, turning three times.

5. Transfer the steaks to a warm plate to rest while the potatoes finish cooking.

6. Put all the dressing ingredients in a jar and shake to emulsify. Divide the tomatoes and rocket between four plates and add the wedges. Drizzle with dressing and serve the steaks on top.

SERVES: 2

Preparation time: **30 minutes**

Cooking time: **20 minutes**

Tuna poke bowl

200 g / 7 oz / ¾ cup sushi rice,
  rinsed and drained

1 ½ tbsp sake

1 pinch stevia

50 ml / 1 ¾ fl. oz / ¼ cup rice vinegar

1 ½ tbsp dark soy sauce

1 tsp manuka honey

1 tsp black sesame seeds

300 g / 10 ½ oz / 2 cups sashimi grade
  tuna, cubed

2 red cabbage leaves, shredded

1 avocado, peeled, stoned and sliced

2 radishes, sliced

⅓ cucumber, cut into thin ribbons

1 handful seaweed salad

1. Put the rice and sake in a saucepan with
   200 ml of cold water. Bring to the boil, then
   reduce the heat to its lowest setting, cover and
   cook for 20 minutes. Turn off the heat and
   rest for 15 minutes with the lid still on.

2. Stir the stevia and $\frac{1}{2}$ a teaspoon of salt into
   the rice vinegar to dissolve. Tip the rice into
   a bowl and stir through the vinegar mixture,
   then cover with a damp cloth while you
   prepare the tuna.

3. Stir the soy sauce, honey and same seeds
   together, then toss with the tuna and leave
   to marinate for 5 minutes.

4. Divide the rice between two bowls and top
   with the tuna, cabbage, avocado, radish,
   cucumber and seaweed.

5. Serve immediately.

SERVES: 4

Preparation time: **20 minutes**

Marinating time: **1 hour**

Cooking time: **35 minutes**

Spicy sweet and sour pork

2 tbsp light soy sauce

50 ml / 1 ¾ fl. oz / ¼ cup manuka honey

2 cloves of garlic, crushed

2 tsp five-spice powder

2 tbsp shaoxing rice wine

1 tbsp sesame oil

600 g / 1 lb 5 ½ oz / 4 cups pork
    tenderloin, sliced

2 tbsp vegetable oil

450 g / 1 lb / 4 cups chantenay carrots

125 ml / 4 ½ fl. oz / ½ cup pure pineapple juice

50 ml / 1 ¾ fl. oz / ¼ cup no-added sugar
    tomato ketchup

1 tsp chilli (chili) flakes

1 tbsp cornflour (cornstarch), slaked with
    2 tbsp cold water

steamed rice, spring onions (scallions) and
    chillies (chilies), to serve

1. Set aside 1 teaspoon of soy sauce and half of
   the honey, then mix the rest with the garlic,
   five-spice, rice wine and sesame oil. Pour the
   mixture into a freezer bag and add the pork
   then seal the bag and massage well to coat.

2. Leave to marinate in the fridge for at least
   1 hour. Meanwhile, preheat the oven to 200°C
   (180°C fan) / 400F / gas 6 and heat the oil in
   a large roasting tin.

3. Roast the carrots for 20 minutes, stirring
   halfway through. Add the pork to the roasting
   tin and roast for another 15 minutes, turning
   after 10 minutes.

4. Meanwhile, heat the pineapple juice, ketchup and
   chilli flakes with the rest of the honey and soy in
   a small saucepan. Add the slaked cornflour and
   stir until it simmers and thickens.

5. Serve the pork on a bed of rice with the carrots
   arranged around the outside.

6. Drizzle over the sauce and serve, scattered with
   sliced spring onions and chillies.

SERVES: 4

Preparation time: **15 minutes**

Cooking time: **35 minutes**

chicken jambalaya

2 tbsp vegetable oil

3 skinless chicken breasts, cut into chunks

1 leek, sliced

1 yellow pepper, diced

2 cloves of cloves, crushed

250 g / 9 oz / 1 ¼ cups long grain rice

1 tbsp Cajun seasoning

400 ml / 14 fl. oz / 1 ²/₃ cups chicken stock

400 g / 14 oz / 1 ²/₃ cups canned
   tomatoes, chopped

150 g / 5 ½ oz / 1 cup frozen peas, defrosted

1. Heat the vegetable oil in a sauté pan and season the chicken with salt and pepper. Brown the chicken pieces all over in the hot oil then remove them from the pan with a slotted spoon and reserve.

2. Add the leeks and peppers to the hot oil and stir-fry for 5 minutes without colouring.

3. Add the garlic and cook for 2 more minutes then stir in the rice and Cajun seasoning.

4. When the rice is well coated with the oil, return the chicken pieces to the pan along with the chicken stock and tomatoes and bring to the boil.

5. As soon as it starts to boil, put the lid on the pan and reduce the heat to low. Leave to cook without lifting the lid for 20 minutes, then stir in the peas, turn off the heat and leave to stand with the lid on for a further 10 minutes.

6. Season to taste with salt and pepper, then serve.

Preparation time: **5 minutes**

Cooking time: **12 minutes**

Salmon and mushroom pasta

200 g / 7 oz / 2 cups dried fusilli pasta

½ tbsp olive oil

½ tbsp butter

150 g / 5 ½ oz / 2 cups button
mushrooms, sliced

75 ml / 2 ½ fl. oz / ⅓ cup dry white wine

200 g / 7 oz / 1 ⅓ cups skinless boneless
salmon fillet, diced

150 ml / 5 ½ fl. oz / ⅔ cup crème fraiche

½ lemon, juiced and zest finely grated

1 handful flat-leaf parsley, chopped

2 tbsp Pecorino, finely grated

1. Boil the pasta in salted water according to
   the packet instructions or until al dente.

2. Meanwhile, heat the oil and butter in a sauté
   pan and fry the mushrooms for 8 minutes or
   until any liquid that emerges evaporates and
   they start to lightly colour.

3. Add the salmon and cook for 1 minute,
   then add the wine and reduce by half.

4. Stir in the crème fraiche, lemon juice and
   lemon zest and season to taste with salt
   and pepper.

5. Drain the pasta and toss it with the sauce,
   then garnish with parsley and Pecorino.

SERVES: 4

Preparation time: **45 minutes**

Cooking time: **15 minutes**

Spaghetti pizza

2 tbsp olive oil

1 onion, finely chopped

2 cloves of garlic, crushed

½ tsp dried chilli (chili) flakes

400 g / 14 oz / 1 ⅔ cups canned
    tomatoes, chopped

1 handful basil leaves, chopped

1 handful flat-leaf parsley, chopped

400 g / 14 oz dried spaghetti

2 large eggs, beaten

100 g / 3 ½ oz / 1 cup mozzarella, grated

1 tomato, sliced

1. Preheat the oven to 220°C (200°C fan) /
   425F / gas 7 and oil a 30 cm (12 in) round
   shallow baking tin.

2. Heat the oil in a saucepan and fry the onion
   over a medium-low heat for 10 minutes or
   until softened and sweet. Add the garlic and
   chilli flakes and stir for 2 more minutes.

3. Pour in the chopped tomatoes, then half-fill
   the can with water and add it to the pan.
   Simmer the sauce for 20 minutes, then stir in
   the herbs and season to taste with salt and
   black pepper.

4. Meanwhile, cook the spaghetti according to
   the packet instructions until al dente. Drain it
   well, then toss with the beaten eggs.

5. Spread the spaghetti into an even layer in
   the prepared tin, then spoon over the sauce.
   Top with a generous layer of mozzarella and
   garnish with sliced tomatoes.

6. Bake the pizza for 15 minutes or until golden
   brown and bubbling. Cut into wedges and
   serve immediately.

Preparation time: **1 hour 15 minutes**

Cooking time: **40 minutes**

Potato, fish and carrot roulade

500 ml / 17 ½ fl. oz / 2 cups milk

300 g / 10 ½ oz undyed smoked haddock fillet

600 g / 1 lb 5 ½ oz potato, peeled and cubed

1 large egg

75 g / 2 ½ oz / ¾ cup Parmesan, finely grated

2 large carrots, coarsely grated

1 small bunch flat leaf parsley, finely chopped

1 tsp raw honey

1 tsp Dijon mustard

½ lemon, juiced

175 g / 6 oz / 1 ¼ cups plain (all-purpose) flour

150 g / 5 ½ oz / 1 ½ cups dried breadcrumbs

1. Bring the milk to the boil, then pour it over the haddock in a bowl. Cover and leave to steep for 10 minutes, then discard the milk, skin and bones and fork the fish into fine flakes.

2. Boil the potatoes for 15 minutes or until tender. Drain well and mash until smooth. Leave to cool until lukewarm, then stir in the haddock, egg and cheese. Leave to cool completely.

3. Mix the carrot and parsley with the honey, mustard and lemon juice. Season with salt and pepper, then set aside. Preheat the oven to 190°C (170°C fan) / 375F / gas 5.

4. Knead the flour into the potato dough, then roll it out into a 1.25 cm (½ in) thick rectangle on a sheet of clingfilm.

5. Squeeze any excess dressing out of the carrot, then spread it on top. Use the clingfilm to help you roll it into a tight roulade, then discard the clingfilm and roll in breadcrumbs to coat.

6. Bake the roulade for 40 minutes or until golden brown and cooked through.

7. Serve with steamed vegetables.

SERVES: 4

Preparation time: **20 minutes**

Cooking time: **3 hours 30 minutes**

Boeuf bourguignon

450 g / 1 lb / 3 cups ox cheek or braising
  steak, cut into large chunks

2 tbsp plain (all-purpose) flour

50 ml / 1 ¾ fl. oz / ¼ cup olive oil

150 g / 5 ½ oz / 1 cup bacon lardons

12 small shallots, peeled

1 carrot, sliced

3 bay leaves

a few sprigs of rosemary

1 small bunch sage

3 cloves of garlic, finely chopped

2 tbsp concentrated tomato puree

700 ml / 1 pint 3 ½ fl. oz / 2 ¾ cups red wine

150 g / 5 ½ oz / 2 cups button mushrooms,
  quartered if large

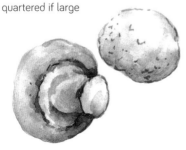

1. Preheat the oven to 160°C (140°C fan) / 325F /
   gas 3.

2. Season the beef with salt and pepper and dust
   the pieces with flour to coat. Heat half the oil
   in a large frying pan and sear the beef in
   batches on all sides. Set aside.

3. Heat the rest of the oil in a cast iron casserole
   dish and fry the lardons, shallots and carrots
   for 5 minutes or until starting to colour.
   Tie the bay leaves, rosemary and sage into
   a bouquet garni with cooking string, then
   add it to the pan with the garlic. Sauté for
   1 minute.

4. Stir in the tomato puree, then pour in the
   wine and bring to the boil.

5. Add the seared beef, then cover the casserole
   and cook in the oven for 3 hours.

6. Add the mushrooms, then return to the oven,
   uncovered, for another 30 minutes. Season to
   taste with salt and pepper before serving.

SERVES : 6

Preparation time: **10 minutes**

Cooking time: **40 minutes**

Chilli con carne

2 tbsp olive oil

1 onion, finely chopped

2 cloves of garlic, crushed

½ tsp cayenne pepper

450 g / 1 lb / 3 cups minced beef

400 g / 14 oz / 2 cups canned tomatoes, chopped

200 ml / 7 fl. oz / ¾ cup beef stock

400 g / 14 oz / 2 cups canned kidney beans, drained

400 g / 14 oz / 2 cups canned black turtle beans, drained

2 large tomatoes, deseeded and diced

1 large green chilli (chili), deseeded and finely chopped

1 shallot, finely chopped

1 lime, juiced

100 ml / 3 ½ fl. oz / ½ cup soured cream

2 tbsp coriander (cilantro) leaves, chopped

1. Heat the oil in a large saucepan and fry the onion for 5 minutes, stirring occasionally. Add the garlic and cayenne and cook for 2 minutes, then add the mince.

2. Fry the mince until it starts to brown then add the chopped tomatoes, stock and beans and bring to a gentle simmer.

3. Cook the chilli con carne for 30 minutes, stirring occasionally, until the mince is tender and the sauce has thickened. Season to taste with salt and pepper.

4. Divide the chilli between six warm bowls. Mix the tomatoes with the chopped chilli, shallot and lime juice, then spoon it on top.

5. Garnish with a spoonful of soured cream and a sprinkle of coriander.

SERVES: 4

Preparation time: **15 minutes**

Cooking time: **5 minutes**

Crispy fish burgers

50 g / 1 ¾ oz / ⅓ cup plain
   (all-purpose) flour

1 egg, beaten

75 g / 2 ½ oz / ¾ cup panko breadcrumbs

4 small portions of pollock fillet

sunflower oil, for deep-frying

4 sourdough buns, halved horizontally

1 red pepper, deseeded and sliced

1 green pepper, deseeded and sliced

¼ small red cabbage, shredded

75 ml / 2 ½ fl. oz / ⅓ cup Greek yogurt

½ tsp chilli (chili) flakes

4 thin slices pecorino

1 handful flat-leaf parsley, stalks removed

1. Put the flour, egg and panko breadcrumbs in three separate bowls. Dip the fish first in the flour, then in the egg, then in the breadcrumbs.

2. Heat the oil in a deep fat fryer, according to the manufacturer's instructions, to a temperature of 180°C (350F).

3. Lower the fish into the hot oil and cook for 5 minutes or until crisp and golden brown. Drain on plenty of kitchen paper.

4. Top the bun bases with sliced peppers and cabbage, then spoon over the yogurt and sprinkle with chilli flakes. Add the crispy fish fillets, followed by the pecorino and parsley

5. Add the bun lids and serve immediately.

Preparation time: **20 minutes**

Cooking time: **1 hour 5 minutes**

Vegetable lasagne

225 g / 8 oz / 3 cups chestnut mushrooms

2 courgettes (zucchini), cut into chunks

1 aubergine (eggplant), cut into chunks

2 tbsp olive oil

1 onion, finely chopped

3 cloves of garlic, crushed

400 g / 14 oz / 1 ²/₃ cups canned
   tomatoes, chopped

1 handful basil, finely chopped

1 handful parsley, finely chopped

450 g / 1 lb fresh lasagne sheets

100 g / 3 ½ oz / 1 cup mild Cheddar, grated

100 g / 3 ½ oz / 1 cup mozzarella, grated

1. Preheat the oven to 200°C (180°C fan) / 400F / gas 6.

2. Put the mushrooms, courgettes and aubergine in a food processor and pulse until the vegetables are finely chopped. The consistency should be similar to cooked mince.

3. Heat the oil in a sauté pan and fry the onion for 10 minutes or until softened. Add the garlic and cook for 2 more minutes. Add the minced vegetables and sauté for 5 minutes.

4. Add the chopped tomatoes and bring to a simmer, then cook over a low heat for 15 minutes. Stir in the herbs and season to taste with salt and pepper.

5. Starting with a layer of lasagne sheets, layer up the ragu, cheeses and pasta in a rectangular baking dish until everything has been used, finishing with a layer of cheese on the top.

6. Bake the lasagne for 30 minutes or until the top is golden and bubbling and the pasta is tender all the way through.

SERVES: 4

Preparation time: **5 minutes**

Cooking time: **50 minutes**

Chicken and chickpea curry

2 tbsp coconut oil

1 onion, finely chopped

1 tbsp fresh root ginger, grated

3 cloves of garlic, crushed

4 skinless chicken breasts, cut into chunks

1 tbsp curry powder

400 g / 14 oz / 1 ²/₃ cups canned coconut milk

400 g / 14 oz / 1 ²/₃ cups canned chickpeas, drained

2 tsp coconut palm sugar

steamed rice, to serve

1. Heat the oil in a large saucepan and fry the onion for 8 minutes stirring occasionally.

2. Add the ginger and garlic and stir-fry for 2 minutes.

3. Add the chicken and cook for 4 minutes or until it starts to brown, then sprinkle over the curry powder and continue to cook for 1 minute.

4. Add the coconut milk and chickpeas and bring to a gentle simmer. If the sauce doesn't cover the chicken, add a little water.

5. Cook the curry for 30 minutes, stirring occasionally, until the chicken is tender and the sauce has thickened.

6. Season to taste with coconut sugar and salt, then serve with steamed rice.

Preparation time: **30 minutes**

Cooking time: **40 minutes**

Spanakopita

2 tbsp olive oil

1 onion, finely chopped

2 cloves of garlic, crushed

100 g / 3 ½ oz / 4 cups young spinach
   leaves, washed

½ tsp nutmeg, freshly grated

75 g / 2 ½ oz / ¾ cup feta cheese, crumbled

1 tbsp mint leaves, chopped

1 tbsp fresh dill, chopped

450 g / 1 lb filo pastry

100 g / 3 ½ oz / ½ cup butter, melted

1. Heat the oil in a large saucepan and fry
   the onion and garlic for 5 minutes without
   colouring. Stir in the spinach until it wilts
   right down, then take the pan off the heat
   and stir in the nutmeg, feta and herbs.
   Season to taste with salt and pepper then
   leave to cool.

2. Preheat the oven to 200°C (180°C fan) /
   400F / gas 6.

3. Brush half of the filo pastry sheets with
   melted butter and use them to line a
   rectangular baking tin. Spoon the filling
   into the centre, then brush the rest of the
   filo with butter and use to make the lid.

4. Bake the pie for 40 minutes or until the
   pastry is golden brown and cooked through
   underneath. Cut into six squares and serve
   hot or at room temperature.

SERVES: 4

Preparation time: **5 minutes**

Cooking time: **15 minutes**

Beef fried rice

2 tbsp vegetable oil

1 large sirloin steak, very thinly sliced

1 onion, sliced

1 red pepper, sliced

2 cloves of garlic, crushed

1 tbsp root ginger, finely chopped

500 g / 17 ½ oz / 3 cups jasmine rice, cooked and cooled

1-2 tbsp light soy sauce

1 tsp sesame oil

cucumber and baby chard leaves, to garnish

1. Heat the oil in a large wok and stir-fry the steak until lightly coloured. Add the onion and peppers and stir-fry for 2 minutes, then add the garlic and ginger and stir-fry for 1 minute or until fragrant.

2. Add the rice and stir-fry until piping hot – this should take about 4 minutes.

3. Season the rice with soy sauce and sesame oil to taste.

4. Divide the rice between four bowls and garnish with cucumber and baby chard leaves.

SERVES: 4

Preparation time: **10 minutes**

Cooking time: **12 minutes**

Chickpea and dill pasta salad

400 g / 14 oz / 4 cups dried fusilli pasta

400 g / 14 oz / 1 ²/₃ cups canned
  chickpeas, drained

150 g / 5 ½ oz / 1 cup frozen peas, defrosted

1 handful mint leaves, chopped

1 handful fresh dill, chopped

2 tbsp brown flax seeds

FOR THE DRESSING

1 tsp manuka honey

1 tsp Dijon mustard

1 lemon, juiced

50 ml / 1 ¾ fl. oz / ¼ cup olive oil

1. Boil the pasta in salted water according to the packet instructions or until al dente. Drain well, then refresh in cold water and drain again.

2. Toss the pasta with the chickpeas, peas, mint, dill and flax seeds.

3. To make the dressing, put all of the ingredients in a small jar with a pinch of salt and pepper and shake until emulsified.

4. Drizzle the dressing over the salad, toss well and serve immediately.

MAKES : 1

Preparation time: **30 minutes**

Rising time: **1 hour**

Cooking time: **12 minutes**

Bacon and sweetcorn pizza

200 g / 7 oz / 1 ⅓ cups strong white bread flour, plus extra for dusting

½ tsp easy blend dried yeast

½ tsp fine sea salt

1 tbsp olive oil

75 ml / 2 ½ fl. oz / ⅓ cup no-added sugar barbecue sauce

100 g / 3 ½ oz / 1 cup mozzarella, grated

4 thin rashers smoked back bacon, halved

1 tomato, sliced

2 tbsp canned sweetcorn, drained

1 red chilli (chili), chopped

1 green chilli (chili), chopped

baby spinach leaves, to garnish

1. Mix together the flour, yeast and salt and stir the oil into 140 ml of warm water. Stir the liquid into the dry ingredients then knead on a lightly oiled surface for 10 minutes or until smooth and elastic.

2. Leave the dough to rest covered with oiled clingfilm for 1–2 hours until doubled in size.

3. Preheat the oven to 220°C (200°C fan) / 425F / gas 7 and grease a non-stick baking tray.

4. Knead the dough for 2 more minutes then roll out thinly into a circle. Transfer the base to the baking tray, spread with half the barbecue sauce and sprinkle with mozzarella.

5. Top the pizza with bacon, tomato and sweetcorn.

6. Bake for 12 minutes or until the pizza dough is cooked through underneath. Drizzle with the rest of the barbecue sauce, sprinkle with chillies and garnish with spinach before serving.

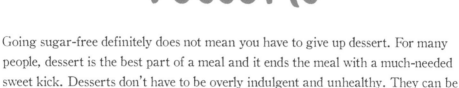

Desserts

Going sugar-free definitely does not mean you have to give up dessert. For many people, dessert is the best part of a meal and it ends the meal with a much-needed sweet kick. Desserts don't have to be overly indulgent and unhealthy. They can be balanced, refreshing, wholesome and still full of flavour.

Refined sugar is present in many shop-bought desserts and many people think that the only sugar-free dessert option is a fruit salad, but it doesn't have to be this way. Make your own delicious desserts using sugar substitutes, such as honey or stevia, and your friends and family won't believe that there is no refined sugar used!

The recipes in this chapter contain no refined sugar but will definitely satisfy any sweet tooth. From Dark Chocolate Brownies and Green Tea Ice Cream to No-bake Cheesecake and Watermelon Ice Lollies, you will love trying out these sugar-free desserts.

Preparation time: **20 minutes**

Cooking time: **35 minutes**

Dark chocolate brownies

100 g / 3 ½ oz / ²/₃ cup sugar-free dark
   chocolate, chopped

85 g / 3 oz / ¾ cup pure cacao powder

225 g / 8 oz / 1 cup butter

450 g / 1 lb / 2 ½ cups coconut palm sugar

4 large eggs

100 g / 3 ½ oz / ²/₃ cup plain
   (all-purpose) flour

strawberries and mint sprigs, to garnish

1. Preheat the oven to 160°C (140°C fan) / 325F /
   gas 3 and oil and line a 20 cm (8 in) square
   cake tin with greaseproof paper.

2. Set aside 2 tablespoons of chopped chocolate.
   Melt the rest of the chocolate with the cacao
   and butter, then leave to cool a little.

3. Whisk the coconut sugar and eggs together
   with an electric whisk for 3 minutes or until
   very light and creamy.

4. Pour in the chocolate mixture and sieve
   over the flour, then fold everything together.

5. Scrape the mixture into the tin and bake
   for 35 minutes or until the outside is set,
   but the centre is still quite soft. Leave to
   cool completely.

6. Melt the reserved chocolate in the microwave,
   then drizzle it over the brownie. Cut into
   squares and serve with strawberries and
   mint sprigs.

SERVES: 6

Preparation time: **15 minutes**

Cooking time: **10 minutes**

Freezing time: **30 minutes - 4 hours**

Green tea ice cream

250 ml / 9 fl. oz / 1 cup canned
　coconut milk

150 g / 5 ½ oz / ¾ cup coconut palm sugar

1 ½ tbsp matcha green tea powder

500 ml / 17 ½ fl. oz / 2 cups double
　(heavy) cream

6 large egg yolks

mint sprigs, to garnish

1. Put the coconut milk and coconut sugar in a small saucepan with a pinch of salt. Stir over a low heat until the sugar has dissolved, then continue to heat until the surface shimmers.

2. Whisk the matcha into the cream and set aside. In a separate bowl, whisk the egg until thick, then gradually incorporate the hot coconut milk. Scrape the mixture back into the saucepan and stir over a low heat until it just starts to thicken.

3. Gradually whisk the coconut custard into the matcha cream. Leave to cool to room temperature, then chill in the fridge.

4. Churn the custard in an ice cream maker, according to the manufacturer's instructions.

5. Alternatively, scrape the custard into a plastic container and freeze for 2 hours. Scrape the semi-frozen mixture into a food processor and blend until smooth, then return to the freezer for 1 hour. Blend again, then freeze until firm.

6. Scoop the ice cream into bowls and garnish with mint sprigs.

SERVES : 2

Preparation time: **5 minutes**

Chilling time: **4 hours**

Chia and coconut pudding

2 tbsp coconut sugar

½ tsp vanilla extract

600 ml / 1 pint / 2 ½ cups canned
   coconut milk

100 g / 3 ½ oz / ½ cup chia seeds

2 ripe nectarines, stoned and sliced

1 handful blueberries

50 g / 1 ¾ oz / ½ cup fresh coconut, sliced

1. Whisk the coconut sugar and vanilla into the coconut milk until dissolved, then stir in the chia seeds.

2. Transfer the bowl to the fridge and leave to thicken for 4 hours, stirring occasionally.

3. Spoon the pudding into two bowls.

4. Top with nectarine, blueberries and coconut.

SERVES: 4

Preparation time: **20 minutes**

Chilling time: **4 hours or overnight**

Chocolate and orange mousse

100 g / 3 ½ oz sugar-free dark chocolate

1 tsp orange-flavoured liqueur

1 tbsp honey

1 tbsp unsweetened cocoa powder, plus more
   to serve

1 orange, zest only

2 egg whites

50 g / 1 ¾ oz low-fat, sugar-free yogurt

1. Place a heatproof bowl over a pan of simmering water, taking care that it does not touch the water. Break up the sugar-free chocolate and gently melt in the bowl adding the Cointreau, honey, cocoa powder and 1 teaspoon of orange zest. Remove from the heat as soon as it has melted and set aside.

2. Whisk the egg whites in a mixer until soft peaks form.

3. Mix together the cooled melted chocolate with the yogurt until combined. Gently fold in a tablespoon of the egg using a metal spoon, before folding in the remaining egg without knocking out the air.

4. Spoon into serving glasses (using your spoon to create a swirl on top as decoration, if desired) and chill for at least 4 hours or preferably overnight.

5. Sprinkle with a little cocoa powder and serve.

SERVES : 6

Preparation time: **15 minutes**

Cooking time: **10 minutes**

Freezing time: **30 minutes - 4 hours**

Coconut ice cream

600 ml / 1 pint / 2 ½ cups canned coconut milk

4 large egg yolks

100 g / 3 ½ oz / ½ cup coconut palm sugar, plus extra for sprinkling

100 g / 3 ½ oz / ¾ cup fresh coconut, grated

sugar-free wafer cigars, to serve

1. Heat the coconut milk in a small saucepan until the surface starts to shimmer.

2. Meanwhile, whisk the egg yolks with the coconut palm sugar until thick. Gradually incorporate the hot coconut milk, whisking all the time, then scrape the mixture back into the saucepan and stir in the grated coconut.

3. Stir the coconut custard over a low heat until it just starts to thicken, then put the base of the pan in cold water and continue to stir until the custard cools a little and the danger of curdling has passed. Leave to cool to room temperature, then chill in the fridge.

4. Churn the custard in an ice cream maker, according to the manufacturer's instructions.

5. Alternatively, scrape the custard into a plastic container and freeze for 2 hours. Scrape the semi-frozen mixture into a food processor and blend until smooth, then return to the freezer for 1 hour. Blend again, then freeze until firm.

6. Scoop the ice cream into bowls and sprinkle with coconut sugar. Serve immediately with wafer cigars.

MAKES: 6

Preparation time: **45 minutes**

Cooking time: **8 minutes**

Dark chocolate fondants

150 g / 5 ½ oz / 1 cup sugar-free dark
   chocolate, chopped

150 g / 5 ½ oz / ²/₃ cup butter, cubed

100 g / 3 ½ oz / ½ cup coconut palm sugar

3 large eggs, plus 3 egg yolks

1 tbsp plain (all-purpose) flour

1. Melt the dark chocolate, butter and coconut
   palm sugar together in a saucepan, stirring to
   dissolve the sugar. Leave to cool a little then
   beat in the eggs and egg yolks. Sieve over and
   fold in the flour.

2. Divide the mixture between six thick muffin
   cases or mini pudding basins, then chill for
   30 minutes.

3. Preheat the oven to 180°C (160°C fan) / 350F /
   gas 4 and put a baking tray in to heat.
   Transfer the fondants to the heated baking
   tray and bake for 8 minutes.

4. Serve immediately.

S E R V E S : 10

Preparation time: **30 minutes**

Chilling time: **2 hours**

No-bake raspberry cheesecake

100 g / 3 ½ oz / ½ cup stevia

2 tsp cornflour (cornstarch)

100 g / 3 ½ oz sugar-free biscuits

1 tbsp unsweetened cocoa powder

50 g / 1 ¾ oz / ¼ cup butter, melted

250 ml / 9 fl. oz / 1 cup double (heavy) cream

450 g / 1 lb / 2 cups cream cheese

1 tsp vanilla extract

300 g / 10 ½ oz / 2 cups raspberries

1. To make an icing sugar substitute, put the stevia in a liquidizer with the cornflour and blend to a fine powder. Set aside.

2. Put the biscuits and cocoa in a food processor and pulse to form fine crumbs. Drizzle in the melted butter and pulse again until the mixture looks like wet sand. Tip the crumbs into a spring-form cake tin and press into an even layer.

3. Whip the cream with an electric whisk until it holds its shape, then set aside. Use the whisk to beat the cream cheese until smooth, then beat in the vanilla extract and all but 2 tablespoons of the icing sugar substitute. Fold in the whipped cream, then spread the mixture evenly over the base.

4. Chill the cheesecake for 2 hours or until set.

5. Meanwhile, press half the raspberries through a sieve to make a seedless sauce and sweeten to taste with some of the reserved icing sugar substitute.

6. Unmould the cheesecake and spoon over the sauce.

7. Garnish with raspberries and, if desired, dust lightly with icing sugar substitute.

SERVES : 6

Preparation time: **20 minutes**

Cooking time: **10 minutes**

Freezing time: **30 minutes - 4 hours**

Blueberry and coconut ice cream

300 g / 10 ½ oz / 2 cups fresh blueberries, plus extra to serve

400 ml / 14 fl. oz / 1 ¾ cups canned coconut milk

4 large egg yolks

100 g / 3 ½ oz / ½ cup coconut palm sugar

28 g / 1 oz / 1 cup unsweetened coconut flakes

sugar-free wafer cigars, to serve

1. Put the blueberries and coconut milk in a liquidizer and blend until smooth. Heat the smoothie mixture in a small saucepan until the surface starts to shimmer.

2. Meanwhile, whisk the egg yolks with the coconut palm sugar until thick. Gradually incorporate the hot smoothie, whisking continually, then scrape the mixture back into the saucepan.

3. Stir the custard over a low heat until it just starts to thicken, then put the base of the pan in cold water and continue to stir until the custard cools a little and the danger of curdling has passed. Leave to cool to room temperature, then chill in the fridge.

4. Churn the custard in an ice cream maker, according to the manufacturer's instructions.

5. Alternatively, scrape the custard into a plastic container and freeze for 2 hours. Scrape the semi-frozen mixture into a food processor and blend until smooth, then return to the freezer for 1 hour. Blend again, then freeze until firm.

6. Scoop the ice cream into bowls and garnish with blueberries, coconut flakes and wafer cigars.

MAKES : 8

Preparation time: **30 minutes**

Chilling time: **1 hour**

Cooking time: **5 minutes**

Strawberry cheesecake pots

100 g / 3 ½ oz / ½ cup stevia

2 tsp cornflour (cornstarch)

100 g / 3 ½ oz sugar-free biscuits

50 g / 1 ¾ oz / ¼ cup butter, melted

250 ml / 9 fl. oz / 1 cup double
    (heavy) cream

450 g / 1 lb / 2 cups cream cheese

1 lemon, juiced and zest finely grated

300 g / 10 ½ oz / 2 cups strawberries, sliced

mint sprigs, to garnish

1. To make an icing sugar substitute, put the stevia in a liquidizer with the cornflour and blend to a fine powder. Set aside.

2. Put the biscuits in a food processor and pulse to form fine crumbs. Drizzle in the melted butter and pulse again until the mixture looks like wet sand. Divide the mixture between eight small jars and press into an even layer.

3. Whip the cream with an electric whisk until it holds its shape, then set aside. Use the whisk to beat the cream cheese until smooth, then beat in the lemon juice, zest and all but 2 tablespoons of the icing sugar substitute. Gently fold in the whipped cream and divide between the jars. Chill for 1 hour.

4. Meanwhile, put half of the strawberries in a saucepan with a splash of water. Cover and simmer for 5 minutes, then stir in 1 tablespoon of the icing sugar substitute. Blend until smooth and leave to cool.

5. Spoon the sauce on top of the cheesecakes and garnish with strawberries and mint sprigs.

MAKES : 500ML

Preparation time: **15 minutes**

Freezing time: **2 hours 30 minutes**

Easy strawberry sorbet

450 g / 1 lb / 3 cups strawberries,
  hulled and quartered

2 tbsp stevia

1 egg white, lightly beaten

mint sprigs, to garnish

1. Spread out two thirds of the strawberries on a lined baking tray and freeze for 2 hours.

2. Transfer the frozen strawberries to a food processor with the stevia and blend until smooth, pausing to scrape down the sides as necessary.

3. Add the egg white and blend again, then scrape the mixture into a plastic tub and freeze for 30 minutes or until firm.

4. Scoop the sorbet into bowls and serve with the rest of the strawberries and a garnish of mint sprigs.

MAKES: 6

Preparation time: **15 minutes**

Freezing time: **3 hours**

Blueberry yogurt ice lollies

300 g / 10 ½ fl. oz / 2 cups blueberries
500 ml / 17 ½ fl. oz / 2 cups Greek yogurt
50 ml / 1 ¾ fl. oz / ¼ cup manuka honey
3 tbsp sugar-free sprinkles, if desired

1. Put two thirds of the blueberries and Greek yogurt in a liquidizer with the honey and blend until smooth. Fold in the rest of the blueberries, then ripple through the rest of the yogurt.

2. Divide the mixture between a 6-hole ice lolly mould and insert a lolly stick into the centre of each one.

3. Freeze for 3 hours or until solid.

4. Dip the outside of the mould briefly in hot water to unmould before serving.

5. If desired, once unmoulded, press the slightly melted ice lollies into sugar-free sprinkles for added texture and decoration.

SERVES: 8

Preparation time: **20 minutes**

Cooking time: **50 minutes**

Apricot cake

225 g / 8 oz / 1 ½ cups self-raising flour

100 g / 3 ½ oz / ½ cup butter, cubed

100 g / 3 ½ oz / ½ cup coconut palm sugar

½ tsp ground cardamom

1 large egg

75 ml / 2 ½ fl. oz / ⅓ cup whole milk

1 tsp vanilla extract

150 g / 5 ½ oz / ¾ cup unsulphured dried
    apricots, finely chopped

fresh apricots and lemon balm, to serve

FOR THE SUGAR-FREE ICING SUGAR

100 g / 3 ½ oz / ½ cup stevia or zylitol

2 tsp cornflour (cornstarch)

1. Preheat the oven to 180°C (160°C fan) /
   350F / gas 4 and line a 20 cm (8 in) round
   spring-form cake tin with greaseproof paper.

2. Sieve the flour into a mixing bowl and rub
   in the butter until it resembles breadcrumbs.
   Stir in the coconut palm sugar and
   ground cardamom.

3. Lightly beat the egg with the milk and vanilla
   extract. Stir it into the dry ingredients with
   the dried apricots until just combined, then
   scrape the mixture into the tin.

4. Bake the cake for 50 minutes or until a skewer
   inserted comes out clean. Transfer the cake to
   a wire rack and leave to cool completely.

5. To make the sugar-free icing sugar, put the
   sweetener in a liquidizer with the cornflour
   and blend until it forms a fine powder.

6. Sprinkle a little of the powder over the cake
   and garnish with quartered fresh apricots
   and lemon balm.

SERVES: 6

Preparation time: **15 minutes**

Chilling time: **4 hours**

Dragon fruit chia pudding

6 red dragon fruit, halved

1 ripe mango, peeled, stoned and diced

250 ml / 9 fl. oz / 1 cup pure
    pomegranate juice

200 g / 7 oz / 1 cup chia seeds

2 tbsp coconut palm sugar

½ tsp vanilla extract

600 ml / 1 pint / 2 ½ cups canned
    coconut milk

mint sprigs, to garnish

1. Use a melon baller to scoop eighteen spheres
   from the dragon fruits and set aside for
   the garnish.

2. Scoop the rest of the dragon fruit flesh into
   a liquidizer with the mango and pomegranate
   juice and blend until smooth. Pour into a
   bowl and stir in half the chia seeds. Transfer
   the bowl to the fridge and leave to thicken
   for 4 hours, stirring occasionally.

3. Whisk the coconut sugar and vanilla into
   the coconut milk until dissolved, then stir in
   the rest of the chia seeds. Transfer the bowl
   to the fridge and leave to thicken for 4 hours,
   stirring occasionally.

4. Divide the dragon fruit pudding between
   six glasses and top with the coconut pudding.
   Garnish with the dragon fruit spheres and
   mint sprigs, then chill until ready to serve.

SERVES: 8

Preparation time: **10 minutes**

Freezing time: **3 hours**

Watermelon ice lollies

900 g / 2 lb / 7 ¼ cups watermelon,
    peeled and deseeded

2 limes, juiced

2 tbsp stevia

1. Cube the watermelon and put in a blender with the lime juice and stevia.

2. Blend until smooth then spoon the mixture into an 8-hole ice lolly mould and add wooden lolly sticks.

3. Freeze for 3 hours or until solid.

4. Dip the outside of the mould briefly in hot water to unmould before serving.

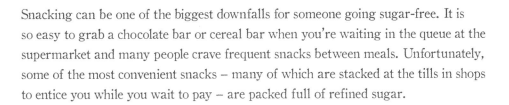

Treats

Snacking can be one of the biggest downfalls for someone going sugar-free. It is so easy to grab a chocolate bar or cereal bar when you're waiting in the queue at the supermarket and many people crave frequent snacks between meals. Unfortunately, some of the most convenient snacks – many of which are stacked at the tills in shops to entice you while you wait to pay – are packed full of refined sugar.

As you change your diet to a slow-burning, nutrient-rich plan, you should start to feel fuller for longer and have fewer cravings. Having said this, there is no reason why you should banish snacks and treats completely.

This chapter will provide you with inspiration for delicious, sugar-free treats which you can snack on during the day, when you really need that extra boost of energy to get you through to the next meal time. From Spiced Oat Biscuits and Seeded Miso Sticks to Fudge Bars and delicious Spiced Cream Muffins, there are several to try out and choose from. Once you have ditched the chocolate bars and sugar-rich biscuits, you will never look back!

Preparation time: **25 minutes**

Cooking time: **20 minutes**

Bacon and broccoli tarts

350 g / 12 ½ oz all-butter puff pastry

1 egg, beaten

225 g / 8 oz / 1 block halloumi, cut horizontally into 6 slices

1 tsp ground sumac

1 tbsp manuka honey

50 ml / 1 ¾ fl. oz / ¼ cup olive oil

8 rashers smoked streaky bacon, cut into short lengths

125 g / 4 ½ oz / 1 cup tenderstem broccoli, cut into florets

2 tbsp pecorino, finely grated

baby salad leaves, to serve

1. Preheat the oven to 220°C (200°C fan) / 425F / gas 7 and line a baking tray with greaseproof paper.

2. Roll out the pastry and cut it into six squares. Cut a 1.25 cm (½ in) border around the outside of each one, leaving two opposite corners uncut, and brush with beaten egg. Pull one of the cut corners across to the other side, followed by the other cut corner to make a raised border, then brush again with egg.

3. Add a slice of halloumi to each one. Stir the sumac and honey into the oil and drizzle half of it over the tarts. Arrange the bacon and broccoli on top.

4. Bake the tarts for 20 minutes or until the pastry is crisp underneath.

5. Sprinkle the tarts with pecorino and serve with baby salad leaves, drizzled with the rest of the sumac dressing.

MAKES : 16

Preparation time: **15 minutes**

Cooking time: **15 minutes**

Seeded miso sticks

400 g / 14 oz all-butter puff pastry

1 tsp plain (all-purpose) flour, for rolling

75 ml / 2 ½ fl. oz / ⅓ cup sweet white miso

2 tbsp sesame seeds

2 tbsp sunflower seeds

2 tbsp hemp seeds

1. Preheat the oven to 220°C (200°C fan) / 425F / gas 7.

2. Roll out the pastry on a lightly floured surface into a large rectangle. Brush the pastry with half the miso and fold it in half.

3. Roll it out a little more, then spread with the rest of the miso. Sprinkle over the seeds and press them down lightly so that they stick.

4. Cut the pastry in half, then cut each half into eight sticks.

5. Bake for 15 minutes or until golden brown and crisp. Transfer to a wire rack and leave to cool a little before serving warm.

Preparation time: **30 minutes**

Cooking time: **5 minutes**

Chilling time: **4 hours**

Chocolate almond fudge bars

175 ml / 6 fl. oz / ⅔ cup double (heavy) cream

2 tbsp manuka honey

200 g / 7 oz / 1 ⅓ cups sugar-free dark chocolate, chopped

50 g / 1 ¾ oz / ¼ cup almond butter

125 g / 4 ½ oz / 1 cup blanched almonds

1. Heat the cream with the honey until it starts to simmer.

2. Put the chopped dark chocolate in a bowl and pour over the hot cream, then stir gently to combine. Leave the ganache to cool a little then stir in the almond butter. If the ganache is not smooth at this stage, use a stick blender to emulsify the mixture.

3. Fold in the blanched almonds, then scrape it into a small silicone loaf mould and level the top.

4. Chill for 4 hours or until firm. Turn the fudge out of the mould and cut it into sixteen bars.

5. Store the bars in the fridge, interleaved with greaseproof paper.

MAKES : 12

Preparation time: **20 minutes**

Cooking time: **15 minutes**

Spiced oat biscuits

100 g / 3 ½ oz / ½ cup butter

75 g / 2 ½ oz / ⅓ cup coconut palm sugar

1 tbsp raw honey

100 g / 3 ½ oz / ⅔ cup self-raising flour

1 tsp ground mixed spice

50 g / 1 ¾ oz / ½ cup hazelnuts, chopped

200 g / 7 oz / 2 cups rolled porridge oats

1. Preheat the oven to 180°C (160°C fan) / 350F / gas 4 and grease two baking trays.

2. Put the butter, coconut palm sugar and honey in a small saucepan and stir over a low heat until the butter melts and the sugar dissolves.

3. Mix the flour with the spice, hazelnuts and half the rolled oats in a bowl. Pour in the butter mixture and stir to combine.

4. Shape the mixture into twelve balls, then flatten them into patties and turn to coat in the rest of the oats.

5. Space the biscuits out on the baking trays and bake for 15 minutes or until golden and crisp. Leave to cool on a wire rack before serving.

Preparation time: **25 minutes**

Cooking time: **20 minutes**

Lemon and chia seed muffins

1 large egg

125 ml / 4 ½ fl. oz / ½ cup sunflower oil

125 ml / 4 ½ fl. oz / ½ cup milk

375 g / 12 ½ oz / 2 ½ cups self-raising flour, sifted

1 tsp baking powder

200 g / 7 oz / 1 ¼ cups coconut palm sugar

2 tbsp chia seeds

1 lemon, juiced and zest finely grated

50 ml / 1 ¾ fl. oz / ¼ cup manuka honey

1. Preheat the oven to 180°C (160°C fan) / 350F / gas 4 and line a 12-hole muffin tin with paper cases.

2. Beat the egg in a jug with the oil and milk until well mixed.

3. Mix the flour, baking powder, coconut palm sugar, chia seeds and lemon zest in a bowl. Pour in the egg mixture and stir just enough to combine.

4. Spoon the mixture into the cases, then bake for 20 minutes or until a skewer inserted comes out clean.

5. Stir the lemon juice into the honey. As soon as the cakes come out of the oven, prick the tops with a skewer several times and drizzle over the syrup.

6. Leave to cool completely on a wire rack before serving.

MAKES: 12

Preparation time: **45 minutes**

Cooking time: **20 minutes**

Spiced cream muffins

1 large egg

125 ml / 4 ½ fl. oz / ½ cup sunflower oil

125 ml / 4 ½ fl. oz / ½ cup skimmed milk

375 g / 12 ½ oz / 2 ½ cups self-raising flour, sifted

1 tsp baking powder

200 g / 7 oz / 1 ¼ cups coconut palm sugar

1 tsp ground cinnamon

1 tsp ground ginger

¼ tsp ground cloves

600 ml / 1 pint / 2 ½ cups double (heavy) cream

2 tbsp sugar-free cake sprinkles

1. Preheat the oven to 180°C (160°C fan) / 350F / gas 4 and line a 12-hole muffin tin with thick paper cases.

2. Beat the egg in a jug with the oil and milk until well mixed.

3. Mix the flour, baking powder, coconut palm sugar and spices in a bowl. Pour in the egg mixture and stir just enough to combine.

4. Spoon the mixture into the cases, then bake for 20 minutes or until a skewer inserted comes out clean. Transfer the cakes to a wire rack and leave to cool completely.

5. Whip the cream until it holds its shape, then spoon it into a piping bag fitted with a large star nozzle. Pipe a big swirl of cream onto each muffin.

6. Sprinkle over the cake sprinkles and serve the same day.

Meal plans and Diary

When starting a new diet, it is important to have a plan. Otherwise you will have a day – probably fairly early on – where you are pressed for time and don't have a menu planned or ingredients bought. It is at times like this when you are likely to reach for something comforting and familiar… and possibly full of sugar.

Before you start, sit down and think about how you want to tackle going sugar-free. How far do you want to reduce your sugar intake each week? You should have a plan for how many grams of sugar you are allowed as you gradually cut it out of your diet.

Also, jot down some targets for exercise and weight loss. It may seem like a lot to think about, but once you get into the swing of things, it will all become second nature.

In this chapter, you can plan and track your progress for six weeks. The ideas and recipes in this book are only the tip of the iceberg as far as delicious sugar-free food is concerned, but they are a great place to start if you're lacking inspiration for sugar-free meals.

Once you have your plan in place and your shopping list written, make sure to keep a record of everything you eat and drink. That way you cannot just 'forget' about that biscuit with your tea or soft drink or glass of wine at a friend's. Before you know it, you will be sugar-free!

Week 1

	Breakfast	Lunch	Snack	Dinner
Monday				
Tuesday				
Wednesday				
Thursday				
Friday				
Saturday				
Sunday				

Starting weight

Finishing weight

How I feel

Exercise log

Week 2

	Breakfast	Lunch	Snack	Dinner
Monday				
Tuesday				
Wednesday				
Thursday				
Friday				
Saturday				
Sunday				

Starting weight

Finishing weight

How I feel	Exercise log

Week 3

	Breakfast	Lunch	Snack	Dinner
Monday				
Tuesday				
Wednesday				
Thursday				
Friday				
Saturday				
Sunday				

Starting weight

Finishing weight

How I feel	Exercise log

week 4

	Breakfast	Lunch	Snack	Dinner
Monday				
Tuesday				
Wednesday				
Thursday				
Friday				
Saturday				
Sunday				

Starting weight

Finishing weight

How I feel	Exercise log

Week 5

	Breakfast	Lunch	Snack	Dinner
Monday				
Tuesday				
Wednesday				
Thursday				
Friday				
Saturday				
Sunday				

Starting weight

Finishing weight

How I feel	Exercise log

Week 6

	Breakfast	Lunch	Snack	Dinner
Monday				
Tuesday				
Wednesday				
Thursday				
Friday				
Saturday				
Sunday				

Starting weight

Finishing weight

How I feel

Exercise log

keeping it off

Congratulations – you've done it! You've stuck to the sugar-free diet and are feeling the benefits already. You have more energy, you feel great and you may have lost some weight too. Now comes the hard part: keeping it off. Many dieters reach their target and then lose the momentum to stick with the new routine. Here are a few tips for keeping motivated:

- Remember why you did it! Have a look at an old photograph of yourself and think about how you felt before you cut out sugar. Keep that old photo handy for whenever you have a craving or are feeling low.

- If you have gone down a dress size, then clear out some of your old clothes and treat yourself to a few things in your new size.